W9-CQN-410

Standards of Practice
for Animal-Assisted Activities
and Animal-Assisted Therapy

November 1996

Sponsored by the
Delta Society®

E-mail: info@deltasociety.org

Website: www.deltasociety.org

Funded in part by grants from
The A.D. Henderson Foundation and
The Max and Victoria Dreyfus Foundation, Inc.

ISBN 1-889785-01-6
Printed in the United State of America

FORWARD

DELTA SOCIETY's activities have expanded to include programs involving individuals and animals providing therapeutic assistance to a variety of populations in various settings. It has become increasingly important to have standards by which to guide these activities. A committee has been formed to accomplish the task of developing standards for animal-assisted activities and animal-assisted therapy (AAA/AAT) at the Delta Society's annual conference in October 1990. A list of these committee members is included in Appendix A.

The standards for AAA and AAT were devised by this committee, along with many other individuals who gave their time and input to these areas of concentration. These standards were developed to meet a variety of needs and to accomplish several purposes:

- To provide a better quality of service to all clients

- To provide a resource for risk management, quality assurance, and safety administration

- To provide guidelines for the planning and organization of new AAA/AAT programs

- To provide an educational resource for staff and personnel orientation and training

- To provide organization and definition on a level consistent with current knowledge and practice

- To provide a means of on-going self-assessment and improvement

- To provide an authoritative source of information for use in program promotion

- To provide evidence to other professional organizations of internal structure and consistency

- To provide for the health, welfare, and safety of animals involved in AAA/AAT programs.

Animal-Assisted Activities and Animal-Assisted Therapy have the potential to attain nationally recognized professional status. The development of standards to regulate the practice of these disciplines is the first step in the enactment of a commitment to provide quality service. The development of these standards clearly indicates that today's AAA/AAT community is willing to monitor its own activities in a professional manner. Such development also indicates that it wants to tackle directly the issue of quality at all levels, and to encourage AAA/AAT practitioners to work toward the highest level of performance in order to achieve an optimal level of therapeutic benefit.

The client represents the basic reason for standards development, for standards implementation, and for the continual re-evaluation and revision that occurs once standards are in place. As a result of these efforts, the future of AAA/AAT is ensured — not only for those who practice in the field, but also for those clients who avail themselves of the services offered. The 'ripple' that spreads from improved services produces direct benefits to clients.

The future of AAA/AAT is truly enhanced by the development and use of these standards. The community at large will view our efforts with heightened respect and admiration for its professionalism and the improved quality of service that is provided.

Jean M. Tebay, MS
Project General Chair
June 1992

ACKNOWLEDGEMENT

DELTA SOCIETY wishes to thank those people who donated their time, expertise, and assistance in the development of the *Standards of Practice*. By sharing personal and professional experiences in the field of human-animal interactions, they have helped us all continue to learn about the benefits of sharing our lives with animals and nature. DELTA SOCIETY hopes that the *Standards of Practice* will encourage the development of more animal-assisted activity and therapy programs and will assist in the continuing improvement of existing programs.

DELTA SOCIETY would like to express its appreciation to the more than fifty people (listed in Appendix A) who spent many hours in the development, revision, and editing of this document. The following people were instrumental in organizing and directing the process of this work as chairpersons of the Standards Committee: Robert Behling, Ph.D. - Administration and Organization; Sherry Kirwin, MA - Volunteers; Bonnie Mader, MS - Health/Human Service Providers; Guy Hancock, D.V.M. - Animals; and Linda Nebbe, MS - Ethics. We would like to thank the following members of the DELTA SOCI-ETY board of directors for their guidance: Lynn Anderson, D.V.M.; Dona Singlehurst; Russel Chapin, D.V.M. and Susan Cohen, ACSW. Several organizations provided important insights and suggestions in their role as test sites: Companion Animal Association of Arizona, Inc., Caring Critters, Inc., and National Capital Therapy Dogs, Inc. Their efforts are greatly appreciated. DELTA SOCIETY would like to express a special appreciation to Shari and Wayne Sternberger for their computer skill and editing expertise in preparing the first document.

DELTA SOCIETY gratefully acknowledges the work of the members of the Animal-Assisted Activities and Therapy Curriculum Development Task Force. Members include: Ellen Shay, MA; Linda Nebbe, MA; Sherry Kirwin, MA; Nancy Jainchill, PhD; Mary Burch, PhD; Judith Gammonley, RN, PhD; Aaron Katcher, MD; Christine M. Hill, M.Ed; Catherine S. Sigler, MA, OTR/L; Sharon Sternberger; Wayne Sternberger, PhD; Maureen Fredrickson, MSW, staff. They gave their time and energy to develop experiential and educational guidelines for personnel in the field of AAA/AAT.

DELTA SOCIETY wishes to thank The Max and Victoria Dreyfus Foundation and The A.D. Henderson Foundation for their generous and timely financial assistance in making *Standards of Practice for AAA/AAT* possible.

This Standards manual is dedicated to Jean M. Tebay, MS, whose vision and leadership encouraged and inspired all who worked on this Standards manual.

Maureen Fredrickson
Delta Society Program Director
November 1996

INTRODUCTION TO THE STANDARDS OF PRACTICE

Our understanding of the human-animal bond remains in its infancy. The positive consequences and outcomes, however, are undeniable. Animal-assisted activities and animal-assisted therapy (AAA/AAT), are realities that are practiced daily in countless settings the world over. The implementation is hardly an exacting science; however, it needs to be approached with a professional attitude in order to ensure reliability and safety. This document has been developed to offer a structured foundation for the field.

As a comprehensive examination of the standards for animal-assisted activities and animal-assisted therapy (AAA/AAT), the *Standards of Practice* serves a diverse audience with a wide range of needs. For example, an *organization* will find a complete basis for establishing or tailoring programs to provide AAA/AAT services in a variety of human service facilities. A *facility* will find extensive information about program expectations and interactions. *Individuals* will find a thorough examination of the experiential and educational requirements of Animal-Assisted Activities and Therapy Specialists. Each user, therefore, will find different sections of interest and significance.

The numbers of topics found in the contents of the *Standards of Practice* should reinforce the diverse nature of AAA/AAT. A simple formula does not exist to integrate clients, animals, handlers, facilities, and human health care providers in an AAA/AAT program that is guaranteed to succeed. The environment that exists is truly dynamic and it evolves simply because of the presence of, and participation by, the animal.

The format is intended to lead the user through the various aspects of AAA/AAT programs and services in order that they may be suitably integrated. The first section focuses on the requirements of a site assessment because the process of identifying advantages and barriers to the practice of AAA/AAT will ultimately determine the success of these services as well as the parameters in which these services function. The second and third sections address the requirements and needs of the personnel involved in delivery of AAA/AAT services. Although an immerging field, AAA/AAT requires specific and specialized skills from providers in order to minimize risks and maximize benefits to recipients. The organizational and administrative processes of provider organizations is covered in depth to ensure a solid foundation for continuous delivery of services. Section four addresses the actual delivery or practice of AAA/AAT services. This section will enable health care providers and lay personnel to critically evaluate the methods by which AAA/AAT is integrated into the recipient's day and to assess the benefits of the services. Documentation and planning is addresses within this section to assure that there is accountability. The needs and requirements of animals are the focus of section five and include considerations for resident animals as well as those that visit. Finally, investigative studies are considered in recognition of the demands for clearly documented clinical evidence of therapeutic benefits of AAA/AAT.

In anticipation of establishing an AAA/AAT program, the *Standards of Practice* serves as a checklist of issues that should be considered and resolved in the planning stage. The interaction of the issues is complex, and the shear number of elements can be overwhelming without such guidance. During the trial phase of a program, the *Standards of Practice* can serve as a resource to assure that expectations are met in a professional manner. To satisfy anticipated accreditation requirements, the *Standards of Practice* manual functions as a formal evaluation worksheet.

Clearly, the level of detail contained in the *Standards of Practice* may not be necessary for all programs or organizations. Similarly, details of the criteria must be tailored for the specific program and organization to meet the self-consistency necessary to satisfy articles of incorporation, by-laws, and local jurisdiction codes. In summary, use the *Standards of Practice* as a living, working document to optimize the ease and effectiveness of meeting the objectives of your program or organization.

An initial exposure to the dynamics of AAA/AAT is found in the process of matching animals and handlers with facilities and clientele. Animals must be screened before being selected to work in AAA/AAT programs and having contact with clients. The screening process assesses the animal's reliability, controllability, predictability, and suitability to the AAA/AAT task, population and working environment. Standards for the animal will be directly linked to the experience and competence of the handler, who may be either a lay volunteer or a professional staff member. Similarly, the standards will be influenced by the task (activities or therapy) that is expected of the animal.

The matrix on the following page has been developed to provide guidance for initial matches between animal/handler teams, facilities, and clientele. The objective of the guidance is to minimize stress on the team while optimizing performance for the client. In the matrix, six visiting *areas* have been identified. Each area is characterized by different facility and client dynamics and variations in the team's experience level. Facility dynamics is a continuum based on four factors:

- *interactions* that are predictable to routinely unpredictable
- *activity levels* that range from low to high
- *distractions* that may be few to many, and
- *staff involvement* that may be basic to a high level.

In addition, the human-animal team (not just the person or solely the animal) capability is a continuum based on three factors:

- *skills* that are basic to specialized
- *visit experience* that is elementary to significant, and
- *staff teaming* that is basic to complex.

The nature of the two continuums suggests that facility and team characteristics will overlap.

This is the first edition of the *Standards of Practice*. Comments received from readers of the draft version (published in July 1992) as well as from the AAT Curriculum Task Force (which met in February 1995) have been incorporated. Your comments and suggestions are welcome and encouraged for inclusion in the second edition.

Wayne Sternberger, PhD
October 1996

Matrix of Environmental Dynamics

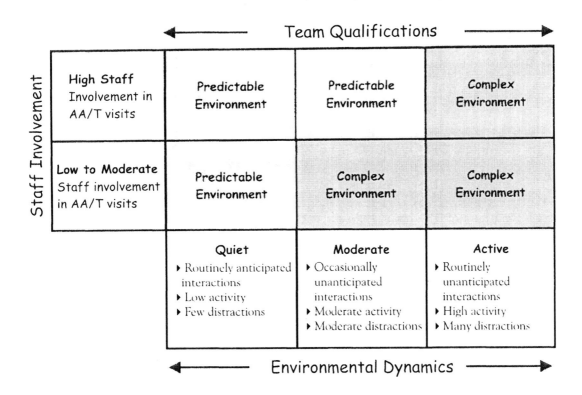

Figure 1.3-1
Team Qualification Matrix

CODE OF ETHICS
For Personnel in Animal-Assisted Activities and Animal-Assisted Therapy

The honor and credibility of a professional lies in their adherence to an exemplary code of ethics set forth as a guide to the members. The purpose of this code is far-reaching because exemplary professional conduct not only upholds honor and dignity, but also enlarges our sphere of usefulness, exults our social standards, and promotes the science we cultivate.

The Delta Society's Code of Ethics is intended to be used as a guide for promoting and maintaining the highest standards of ethical behavior. The code applies to all Animal-Assisted Therapy/Animal-Assisted Activities personnel, whether volunteer or professional. Acceptance of membership in the Delta Society implies adherence to these principles.

1. Animal-Assisted Activities and Animal-Assisted Therapy personnel will perform duties commensurate with their position and training.

2. Animal-Assisted Activities and Animal-Assisted Therapy personnel will abide by the professional ethics of their respective professions and organizations.

3. Animal-Assisted Activities and Animal-Assisted Therapy Personnel will demonstrate a belief and attitude of reverence for all life.

4. Animal-Assisted Activities and Animal-Assisted Therapy personnel will, at all times, treat all, the animals, the people, and the environment, with respect, dignity, and sensitivity, maintaining the quality of life and experience for all involved.

5. Animal-Assisted Activities and Animal-Assisted Therapy personnel will be informed and educated on the aspects and issues related to Animal Assisted Activities and Therapy.

6. Animal-Assisted Therapy and Animal-Assisted Activities personnel will demonstrate commitment, responsibility, and honesty in all phases of their activities.

7. Animal-Assisted Activities and Animal-Assisted Therapy Personnel will be responsible for complying with local, state, and federal laws and Delta Society Policies governing Animal-Assisted Activities and Animal-Assisted Therapy.

8. Each individual and organization will establish or adopt written guidelines to assure a quality program. All programs need to be continuously evaluated and, when appropriate, improved to assure quality standards and service.

CONTENTS

Animal-Assisted Activities—This dog and Volunteer Animal Handler visit a client in a nursing home. *(Photo courtesy of Frank Siteman.)*

Standards of Practice for AAA/AAT

Section 1: Standards for Facility Assessment

The incorporation of animals in educational, medical, residential and rehabilitation facilities alters institutional processes and human relationships. Without careful consideration of the ways an animal's presence can affect the working of each setting, risks to people and animals are increased and potential benefits can be minimized. This section provides a thorough assessment of the interplay between the needs of the animals, handlers, staff, clients/patients/students and the facility. This section will identify advantages and barriers to AAA/AAT within a facility or unit.

Includes:

1.1   Physical Characteristics

1.2   Client Population

1.3   Administrative Support

1.4   Staff Assessment

Standard 1.1:   Physical Characteristics

STANDARD: AAA/AAT is structured to accommodate the physical layout of the facility and provide safety for activities and interactions between animals and people.

RATIONALE: Adequate physical facilities are necessary to ensure safe conduct of AAA/AAT. Such factors as space, lighting and physical design directly affect the types and numbers of animals involved and the kind of services that can be provided. (Note: See Appendix B for sample forms.)

Meets Criterion	Needs Attention	Criteria	
❏	❏	1.1.1	Facility assessment shall identify the physical characteristics and potential for AAA/AAT programs prior to implementation.
❏	❏	1.1.2	The design of the facility shall not present a danger to people or animals involved in AAA/AAT programs.
❏	❏	1.1.3	The species, number of animals involved, and number of clients participating in each session shall be designated and appropriate for the facility.

Meets Criterion	Needs Attention	Criteria	
❑	❑	1.1.4	Areas in which animals are allowed shall be accessible to animals and people.
❑	❑	1.1.5	All entrance and exit doors, stairwells, and elevators that are available for the transport of animals within the facility shall be assessed for safety.
❑	❑	1.1.6	Adequate access to the outdoors for animals shall be available.
❑	❑	1.1.7	Client access to outdoors shall be identified.
❑	❑	1.1.8	Facility dynamics affecting AAA/AAT shall be identified (i.e., shift changes, meal times, etc.).
❑	❑	1.1.9	The facility assessment shall identify additional distractions that could impact AAA/AAT.
❑	❑	1.1.10	The facility assessment shall identify environmental concerns and propose a method of mitigating those concerns.

Standard 1.2: **Client Population**

STANDARD: AAA/AAT is structured to accommodate special needs of the client population and to provide for safe interactions between animals and people.

RATIONALE: Appropriate accommodations must be made for the client population receiving AAA/AAT services. For example, various populations will have differing needs for physical space depending upon equipment being used or attached to the client. Some populations may tolerate active animals, while others may require quiet, gentle animals. In order to assure safety of both clients and animals, client population characteristics must be assessed and planned for before animals enter a facility. These characteristics directly affect the types and numbers of animals involved and the types of services that can be provided. (Note: See Appendix B for sample forms and Section 3.2: Individual Client Assessment.)

Meets Criterion	Needs Attention	Criteria	
❑	❑	1.2.1	Client population assessment shall identify the population characteristics and their potential impact on AAA/AAT services prior to implementation.
❑	❑	1.2.2	The potential for danger to animals inflicted by the client population shall be identified. Methods to minimize this danger shall be identified and implemented.
❑	❑	1.2.3	Potential health risk to animals and people and techniques for reducing this risk shall be identified.
❑	❑	1.2.4	The species, number of animals involved, and characteristics of clients participating in each session shall be designated and suitable for the client population.
❑	❑	1.2.5	Areas of collateral support shall be identified and encouraged.
❑	❑	1.2.6	A client pet history, minimally including allergies, phobias, and likes/dislikes, shall be included in client population assessments.

Standard 1.3: **Administrative Support**

STANDARD: The facility's administrative policies and procedures reflect inclusion of AAA/AAT services.

RATIONALE: Policies and procedures are necessary for any program to run smoothly and to evaluate success. In addition, policies and procedures provide structure for efficient provision of service. Some facilities will already have a mission and administrative attitude which easily accommodates AAA/AAT services. Other facilities will require more persuasion to see how AAA/AAT may be beneficial to their clients. Knowing a facility's mission and providing a thorough AAA/AAT policy provides credibility. (Note: See Appendix B for sample forms.)

Meets Criterion	Needs Attention	Criteria	
❑	❑	1.3.1	The facility's mission shall be identified, as it will impact AAA/AAT.
❑	❑	1.3.2	The facility's administrative policies which relate to or affect AAA/AAT shall be identified.
❑	❑	1.3.3	Health department regulations which relate to or affect AAA/AAT shall be identified. Policies and procedures which address these regulations shall be implemented.
❑	❑	1.3.4	State and federal laws which relate to or affect animals in the facility shall be identified. Policies and procedures which address these laws shall be implemented.
❑	❑	1.3.5	Administrative attitudes which relate to or affect AAA/AAT shall be identified.

Standard 1.4: Staff Assessment

STANDARD: AAA/AAT services are structured to accommodate special needs of the staff.

RATIONALE: Accommodations must be made for the staff working in a facility receiving AAA/AAT services. Staff members may support or sabotage AAA/AAT services. Identifying key people and crucial concerns in advance can help the process of implementing services go smoothly. (Note: See Appendix B for sample forms.)

Meets Criterion	Needs Attention	Criteria	
❑	❑	1.4.1	Staff assessment shall identify staff needs and concerns prior to AAA/AAT services implementation.
❑	❑	1.4.2	Key staff members who can be instrumental in support of AAA/AAT shall be identified.
❑	❑	1.4.3	Key staff members who can be crucial to AAA/AAT operations shall be identified.

Meets Criterion	Needs Attention	Criteria	
❏	❏	1.4.4	Staff training needs regarding AAA/AAT shall be identified.
❏	❏	1.4.5	A staff liaison or program coordinator shall be identified.
❏	❏	1.4.6	Staff-to-client ratios during AAA/AAT delivery shall be identified.
❏	❏	1.4.7	Personnel responsible for AAA/AAT documentation shall be identified.
❏	❏	1.4.8	Staff workload during AAA/AAT delivery shall be identified.

Animal-Assisted Therapy—An Animal-Assisted Therapy Specialist (Social Worker) is assisted by a cat during a session with a client (*Photo courtesy of Frank Siteman*)

Section 2: Standards for AAA/AAT Providers

Individuals, both paid and unpaid, professional and volunteer may contract with facilities to provide AAA/AAT services. This section provides guidelines for AAA/AAT service providers.

Includes:

2.1	Standards for Individual Providers
2.2	Compliance with Laws and Regulations
2.3	Risk Management
2.4	Personnel
	2.4.1 AAT Specialists
	2.4.2 AAA Specialists
	2.4.3 Animal Handlers
2.5	Communication Pathways

Standard 2.1: Standards for Individual Providers

STANDARD: Individual Providers meet educational, experiential, and procedural requirements for AAA/AAT services.

RATIONALE: Individual providers can be paid or unpaid, professional or volunteer. Individual providers have the same responsibilities to animals, recipients and staff as provider organizations do.

Meets Criterion	Needs Attention	Criteria	
❏	❏	2.1.1	Individual providers maintain credentialing through a professional, or volunteer organization involved in AAA/AAT.
❏	❏	2.1.2	Individual providers maintain screening and certification for the animals they work with.

Meets Criterion	Needs Attention	Criteria	
❏	❏	2.1.3	Animals working with individual providers are screened by an impartial evaluator familiar with the settings in which the animals work.
❏	❏	2.1.4	Individual providers maintain insurance for documentation of AAA/AAT services.

Standard 2.2: **Compliance with Laws and Regulations**

STANDARD: The providers are in compliance with local, state, and federal laws and regulations which concern the presence of animals in various settings.

RATIONALE: Compliance with local, state, and federal laws and regulations ensure safety and the acceptance and continuance of AAA/AAT.

Meets Criterion	Needs Attention	Criteria	
❏	❏	2.2.1	The provider shall comply with all laws and regulations which apply to the conduct of AAA/AAT services and the presence of animals in various settings.
❏	❏	2.2.2	The provider shall identify procedures to maintain compliance with these laws and regulations (e.g., identification of areas prohibited to animals).
❏	❏	2.2.3	The provider shall provide training for all personnel regarding the above procedures.
❏	❏	2.2.4	Any variances, changes, or waivers from these laws and regulations shall be identified and documented, and shall be communicated to relevant personnel.

Standard 2.3: **Risk Management**

STANDARD: AAA/AAT services are designed and delivered to minimize risk for all involved.

RATIONALE: To ensure quality, to reduce liability, and to provide for the well-being of all participants, including clients, visitors, volunteers, and animals, a risk management plan is implemented. In the areas of education and human services, it is important to provide services that first and foremost do no harm, and with careful attention to human and animal needs, facilitate positive response and improvement.

Meets Criterion	Needs Attention	Criteria	
❏	❏	2.3.1	Risk management policies and procedures to safeguard the health and welfare of all participating people and animals are maintained by the facility receiving services.
❏	❏	2.3.2	The facility receiving AAA/AAT services shall provide and require adherence to documented policies and procedures for risk management review.
❏	❏	2.3.3	Risk management planning shall utilize applicable OSHA regulations for minimum levels of worker protection.
❏	❏	2.3.4	The provider organization/provider program shall maintain written documentation of up-to-date liability coverage for providers of AAA/AAT services (both paid and volunteer).

Standard 2.4: **Personnel**

Standard 2.4.1: Standards for Animal-Assisted Therapy Specialists

To facilitate consistency in interpretation, the following definition will be used. An **Animal-Assisted Therapy Specialist** is an education/human service provider who delivers and/or directs Animal-Assisted Therapy (AAT). The AAT Specialist has expertise in incorporating animals as an intervention and is knowledgeable about animals. The AAT Specialist is licensed and/or recognized by a separate education or human service professional discipline. This individual complies with the legal and ethical requirements of his/her profession as well as local, state, and federal laws relating to this work.

Standard 2.4.1A: *Credentials*

STANDARD: AAT Specialists meet the credentials and/or licensure required by their profession to deliver specific services, and/or direct volunteers and/or paraprofessionals within AAT settings.

RATIONALE: To ensure that AAT Specialists operate within the scope of practice of their discipline, they shall maintain current educational, legal, and professional credentials. AAT Specialists shall be legally culpable within their professional field.

Meets Criterion	Needs Attention	Criteria	
❑	❑	2.4.1A.1	AAT Specialists' professional credentials shall be valid, as specified within the profession's jurisdiction.
❑	❑	2.4.1A.2	Documentation of current, valid licensure or credentials shall be available upon request.
❑	❑	2.4.1A.3	AAT Specialists shall practice within the scope of the education/human service profession by which they are licensed or credentialed.

Standard 2.4.1B: *Skills*

STANDARD: AAT Specialists have expertise in incorporating animals in treatment and/or educational interventions. They are knowledgeable about the impact of animal interactions on client populations and facility dynamics.

RATIONALE: The practice of animal-assisted interactions requires understanding of how to incorporate animals in a way that enhances human health, well-being and levels of functioning while not compromising animal health and well-being. The skills and knowledge incorporated in practice involved ensure movement toward specified goals.

Meets Criterion	Needs Attention	Criteria	
❑	❑	2.4.1B.1	AAT Specialists shall demonstrate knowledge of humane animal training methods.
❑	❑	2.4.1B.2	AAT Specialists shall demonstrate humane animal handling skills.

Meets Criterion	Needs Attention	Criteria
❑	❑	**2.4.1B.3** AAT Specialists shall demonstrate knowledge of animal housing and management practices.
❑	❑	**2.4.1B.5** AAT Specialists shall perform treatment evaluations for all clients receiving services.
❑	❑	**2.4.1B.6** AAT Specialists directing paraprofessionals or services. —Volunteer animal handlers shall observe and evaluate these interactions on a regular basis.
❑	❑	**2.4.1B.8** AAT Specialists shall determine individualized client goals.
❑	❑	**2.4.1B.9** AAT Specialists shall determine contraindications for AAT.
❑	❑	**2.4.1B.10** AAT Specialists shall interface with the community by providing information to the public including the use of public education presentations.
❑	❑	**2.4.1B.11** AAT Specialists shall use risk management practices.

Standard 2.4.1C: *Continuing Education*

STANDARD: AAT Specialists meet continuing education requirements as established by their profession, agency, and/or licensing body. AAT Specialists are familiar with animal behavior, care, and training techniques and recent developments in the field of AAA/AAT.

RATIONALE: To ensure excellence in quality of care, AAT Specialists shall participate in regular continuing education programs, including those that present information on animals and AAA/AAT.

Meets Criterion	Needs Attention	Criteria
❑	❑	**2.4.1C.1** The AAT Specialist shall provide documentation of continuing education attendance applicable to the specialist's profession.

Meets Criterion	Needs Attention	Criteria	
❏	❏	2.4.1C.2	Continuing education shall be applicable to AAT.
❏	❏	2.4.1C.3	Continuing education shall be applicable to animal care, training, or behavior.

Standard 2.4.2: Animal-Assisted Activity Specialists

To facilitate consistency in interpretation, the following definition will be used. An **Animal-Assisted Activity Specialist** is a person who provides Animal-Assisted Activities (AAA). The AAA Specialist possesses specialized knowledge of animals and the populations with which they interact in delivering motivational, informational, and/or recreational animal-oriented activities.

Standard 2.4.2A: *Credentials*

STANDARD: AAA Specialists have the appropriate credentials to deliver specific services and/or direct volunteers and/or paraprofessionals within AAA settings.

RATIONALE: To ensure that AAA Specialists operate within the scope of practice of their many different disciplines, they shall maintain educational, legal, and professional credentials and be legally culpable within their discipline.

Meets Criterion	Needs Attention	Criteria	
❏	❏	2.4.2A.1	AAA Specialist credentials shall be valid.
❏	❏	2.4.2A.2	Documentation of current, valid licensure or credentials shall be available upon request.
❏	❏	2.4.2A.3	AAA Specialists shall practice within the scope of the profession of which they are a member.

Standard 2.4.2B: *Skills*

STANDARD: The AAA Specialist possesses specialized knowledge of animals and the populations with which they interact in delivering motivational, informational or recreational animal-oriented activities.

RATIONALE: Animal-Assisted Activities provide an opportunity for improving recipients' quality of life and sense of well-being. AAA Specialists must have skills and knowledge of human-animal interactions to ensure maximum benefits and mutually beneficial contacts.

❏   ❏   2.4.2B.1   AAA Specialists shall demonstrate knowledge of humane training and correction techniques.

❏   ❏   2.4.2B.2   AAA Specialists shall demonstrate humane animal handling skills.

❏   ❏   2.4.2B.2   AAA Specialists shall develop and implement observation/data collection techniques.

❏   ❏   2.4.2B.2   AAA Specialists shall develop and implement evaluation procedures.

❏   ❏   2.4.2B.2   AAA Specialists shall interface with the team.

❏   ❏   2.4.2B.2   AAA Specialists shall provide and/or receive referrals.

❏   ❏   2.4.2B.2   AAA Specialists shall exhibit strong interpersonal skills.

❏   ❏   2.4.2B.2   AAA Specialist shall implement collaborative and team with other specialties, volunteers, etc.

❏   ❏   2.4.2B.2   AAA Specialists shall provide recommendations related to client selection for AAA.
—Assess client needs
—Assess client appropriateness for AAA
—Determine contraindications for AAA
—Evaluate effectiveness of AAA

❏   ❏   2.4.2B.2   AAA Specialists shall interface with the community, providing information to the public.

❏   ❏   2.4.2B.2   AAA Specialists shall develop, implement, evaluate, and revise risk management policies.

Standard 2.4.2C: *Continuing Education*

STANDARD: AAA Specialists meet continuing education requirements as established by their profession, agency, and/or licensing body. AAA Specialists are also familiar ,with animal behavior, care, and training techniques and current developments in the field of AAA/AAT.

RATIONALE: To ensure excellence in quality of care, AAA Specialists shall participate in regular continuing education programs, including those that present information on animals and AAA/AAT.

Meets Criterion	Needs Attention	Criteria	
❏	❏	2.4.2C.1	The AAA Specialist shall provide documentation of continuing education attendance in the specialist's discipline.
❏	❏	2.4.2C.2	Continuing education shall be applicable to AAA.
❏	❏	2.4.2C.3	Continuing education shall be applicable to animal care, training, or behavior.

Standard 2.4.3: Animal Handlers

STANDARD: All animal handlers are adequately trained and prepared in handling animals in AAA/AAT settings. Animal handlers understand their role in AAA/AAT and maintain appropriate credentials. An animal handler demonstrates respect for his/her animal teammate.

RATIONALE: In order to work most effectively, animal handlers must have knowledge about and demonstrate skills in animal behavior, training, humane handling, and the ways animals impact people. AAA and AAT sessions are not animal training sessions. Handlers must work with the animal in a way that promotes the perception of the team's reliability, controllability, predictability, and inspires confidence.

Meets Criterion	Needs Attention	Criteria	
❏	❏	2.4.3.1	Animal handlers shall avail themselves of continuing education (both initial and ongoing) about AAA/AAT and animal care and training.

Meets Criterion	Needs Attention	Criteria	
❏	❏	2.4.3.2	Animal handlers shall maintain animals in excellent health and shall not work an animal who shows signs of ill health, discomfort, or reluctance to work.
❏	❏	2.4.3.3	Animal handlers shall maintain animal health, skills, aptitude, and other screenings. Records of screenings shall be available upon request.
❏	❏	2.4.3.4	Animal handlers shall demonstrate skill in animal training and humane animal handling.
❏	❏	2.4.3.5	Animal handlers shall demonstrate knowledge of signs of animal stress.
❏	❏	2.4.3.6	Animal handlers shall demonstrate skill in sharing their animal teammate appropriately with the client population(s) being seen.
❏	❏	2.4.3.7	Animal handlers shall maintain confidentiality.
❏	❏	2.4.3.8	Animal handlers shall provide regular input to the facility. This includes documentation of credentials, visit summaries, and incident reports.
❏	❏	2.4.3.9	Animal handlers shall maintain recognized credentials, as applicable.
❏	❏	2.4.3.10	Animal handlers shall represent themselves accurately to providers and/or facilities.
❏	❏	2.4.3.11	Animal handlers shall report to the facility and the credentially body all incidents involving their animal which may directly or indirectly affect public health and safety.

Standard 2.5: **Communication Pathways**

STANDARD: Records of all AAA/AAT interactions are maintained by the provider and facility.

RATIONALE: To achieve provider credibility and consistency by providing a plan for clear communication paths, confidentiality requirements, and details of information-access procedures.

Meets Criterion	Needs Attention	Criteria	
❏	❏	2.5.1	A chronological record of visits that includes names of participants and interactions that occurred, client responses, notation of other significant occurrences, and suggestions for future interactions or follow-up is maintained by the provider.
❏	❏	2.5.2	The above items shall be documented in the client's official record or chart by the education/human service provider.
❏	❏	2.5.3	Advance notification procedures to communicate changes in AAA/AAT schedules or in-transit delays that may affect interaction expectations is maintained by the provider.
❏	❏	2.5.4	Client request and consent forms shall be provided by the facility.
❏	❏	2.5.5	Procedures that ensure confidentiality of interactions between AAA/AAT providers and clients shall be maintained by the provider and facility.
❏	❏	2.5.6	The client shall have access to true or exact copies of records, but the records remain the confidential property of the provider and/or facility.
❏	❏	2.5.7	All clinical records shall be the property of the facility or primary AAA/AAT provider and shall be maintained and owned as specified by the governing body of the facility.

Section 3: **Standards for Provider Organizations**

Independently incorporated organizations may coordinate visits of professional or volunteer personnel and animals to a number of different facilities. AAA/AAT services can be provided by the facility through a program specifically formed to govern and oversee these services.

Includes:

3.1   Governing Body

3.2   Advisory Committee

3.3   Fiscal Responsibility

3.4   Policies and Procedures

3.5   Inter-Agency Communication

3.6   Personnel

     3.6.1   Orientation and Training

     3.6.2   Staff

     3.6.3   Volunteers

     3.6.4   Volunteer Agreements

3.7   Performance Evaluations

     3.7.1   Policies and Procedures

     3.7.2   AAA/AAT Specialist Evaluations

     3.7.3   Volunteer Evaluations

Standard 3.1:   **Governing Body**

STANDARD: The provider organization or program of the facility providing AAA/AAT services is governed by an organizational structure. Examples include paid or volunteer boards of directors, committees, sub-committees, and/or task forces.

RATIONALE: An administrative system of checks and balances is essential for ensuring AAA/AAT service quality and enhancing periodic review. The governing body may function only for the provider organization, provider program, or it may be the board for the facility which AAA/AAT services are provided.

Meets Criterion	Needs Attention	Criteria	
❏	❏	3.1.1	The provider organization or provider program shall have a governing body, and shall show evidence of an administrative structure.
❏	❏	3.1.2	The governing body shall be aware of the AAA/AAT services, their goals, and operations.
❏	❏	3.1.3	The AAA/AAT coordinator or designated contact person shall have access to the governing body.
❏	❏	3.1.4	The governing body and the AAA/AAT coordinator shall have clear lines of communication and responsibility.
❏	❏	3.1.5	The governing body shall have written policies and procedures describing its role in the provider organization or the provider program.
❏	❏	3.1.6	The AAA/AAT coordinator shall report to the governing body as required.
❏	❏	3.1.7	The AAA/AAT coordinator or designee shall maintain copies of the reports submitted to the governing body.
❏	❏	3.1.8	The AAA/AAT body shall establish the mission and policies for AAA/AAT services, and may advise or oversee the performance of the coordinator.

Standard 3.2: **Advisory Committee**

STANDARD: In addition to a governing body, the provider organization/provider program within the facility may have an advisory committee, which is approved by the governing body.

RATIONALE: An advisory committee is composed of community members and/or facility professionals that are supportive of the goals and objectives of AAA/AAT and are able to assist the provider organization or provider program in areas of specific need. Such needs may include finances, public relations, accounting, grant writing, education, and technical expertise. Advisory committee members need not be employed in a field related to animals. In fact, it may be helpful for members to represent a diverse cross-section of professions.

Meets Criterion	Needs Attention	Criteria	
❏	❏	3.2.1	The advisory committee shall be responsible to the governing body.
❏	❏	3.2.2	The provider organization/provider program shall maintain a list of appropriate professions to be represented on an advisory committee.
❏	❏	3.2.3	The provider organization/provider program shall maintain a list of community members who could serve as members of the advisory committee.
❏	❏	3.2.4	A system shall be in place and functioning for soliciting assistance from key individuals and organizations.
❏	❏	3.2.5	The advisory committee shall have a chair to be responsible, responsive, and available. The chair shall report to the coordinator on a regular basis.

Standard 3.3: **Fiscal Responsibility**

STANDARD: The provider organization/provider program maintained a fiscal plan for operation of AAA/AAT services.

RATIONALE: To ensure continuation of services, provide for stability, and maintain viability, the governing body shall provide overall fiduciary responsibility.

Meets Criterion	Needs Attention	Criteria	
❏	❏	3.3.1	The governing body shall provide evidence of quarterly fiscal reports.
❏	❏	3.3.2	The governing body shall provide plans for an annual outside audit of fiscal affairs.

Meets Criterion	Needs Attention	Criteria	
❑	❑	3.3.3	The governing body shall provide written fiscal policies regarding check writing, purchasing, and reporting of fiscal matters, including those to local, state, and federal authorities as required.
❑	❑	3.3.4	A designated person shall maintain all fiscal records including, but not limited to, contracts, letters of agreement, insurance, and equipment.
❑	❑	3.3.5	The governing body shall continually review and approve the expenditures and sources of funding for delivery of AAA/AAT services.
❑	❑	3.3.6	This financial review shall include management of the budget process, including receipts and expenditures, and decisions regarding the investment of funds such as endowments.

Standard 3.4: **Policies and Procedures**

STANDARD: The provider maintains written records of AAA/AAT policies, procedures, and operations.

RATIONALE: Written records help ensure proper and professional operation. Records provide information for performance evaluations, document services provided, and verify qualifications of AAA/AAT service providers.

Meets Criterion	Needs Attention	Criteria	
❑	❑	3.4.1	The coordinator or designee shall be responsible for the development and implementation of policies and procedures which govern AAA/AAT services, including all necessary records and official documents.
❑	❑	3.4.2	Written policies and procedures which include records management and disposal.

Meets Criterion	Needs Attention	Criteria	
		3.4.3	The program shall have written procedures addressing:
❑	❑		*Quality Assurance* - includes volunteer and staff training (initial and on-going), staff involvement, client participation.
❑	❑		*Risk Management and Safety* - includes program logistics, animal screening (health, skills, aptitude), emergency proceedures.
❑	❑		*Utilization Review* - includes efficiency, effectiveness, efficacy are maintained.
❑	❑	3.4.4	All records shall be secure and available only to designated personnel.
❑	❑	3.4.5	Historical records shall be kept in accordance with the statute of limitations, a minimum of three years.
❑	❑	3.4.6	A person shall be designated to make regular computer back-ups when crucial records are maintained on computer disc.
❑	❑	3.4.7	Administrative records containing confidential material shall require a signed release statement from the client and special procedures prior to release to any individual or organization.
❑	❑	3.4.8	Current documentation of personnel and animal credentials shall be maintained.
❑	❑	3.4.9	Written procedures governing client-animal interactions are maintained.
❑	❑	3.4.10	Written procedures are reviewed by the coordinator or designee on a regular basis.

Standard 3.5: Inter-Agency Communication

STANDARD: AAA/AAT providers and the management of facilities receiving AAA/AAT services shall communicate regularly.

RATIONALE: Open and clear communication between the provider and those receiving services ensures effective operation.

Meets Criterion	Needs Attention	Criteria	
❑	❑	3.5.1	The provider and facility receiving services shall provide a regular plan for communication.
❑	❑	3.5.2	The provider organization/provider program provides contingency planning procedures for emergencies and unplanned incidents.

Standard 3.6: Personnel

Standard 3.6.1: Orientation and Training

STANDARD: The provider organization or provider program provides orientation and training to personnel, both paid and volunteer.

RATIONALE: Clear and comprehensive orientation information needs to be provided to all personnel in order to ensure satisfactory performance. This may include continuing education topics required for successful performance.

Meets Criterion	Needs Attention	Criteria	
❑	❑	3.6.1.1	The provider organization/provider program shall provide orientation and training materials for all personnel, both paid and volunteer.
❑	❑	3.6.1.2	Personnel training shall address consideration for the individual needs and rights of clients.
❑	❑	3.6.1.3	The provider organization/provider program shall document completion of training.

Meets Criterion	Needs Attention	Criteria	
❏	❏	3.6.1.4	Orientation shall take place upon entry into the provider organization/provider program, before beginning work.
❏	❏	3.6.1.5	The provider organization/provider program shall provide and adhere to a plan for reviewing, evaluating, and updating the orientation procedures and materials on a regular basis.
❏	❏	3.6.1.6	Regular, on-going in-service training shall be provided for all personnel.
❏	❏	3.6.1.7	Staff of facilities receiving AAA/AAT services who are impacted by AAA/AAT shall receive in-service training on a regular basis.
❏	❏	3.6.1.8	A system for receiving on-going staff suggestions shall be implemented.
❏	❏	3.6.1.9	A system for communication between staff impacted by AAA/AAT and AAA/AAT providers shall be established.
❏	❏	3.6.1.10	Procedures for identifying and discontinuing unwanted interactions or inappropriate behavior between clients and animals or clients and other people are identified.

Standard 3.6.2: Staff

STANDARD: A coordinator oversees the delivery of AAA/AAT services. The coordinator may require supervisory staff, paid or volunteer, to assist in daily operations.

RATIONALE: To ensure quality and effectiveness of service delivery, the coordinator's job description is based on the needs of the provider organization/provider program and meets all requirements set by the governing body.

Meets Criterion	Needs Attention	Criteria	
❏	❏	3.6.2.1	A clear job description is provided for the coordinator.
❏	❏	3.6.2.2	A plan for determining the need for increasing staff and/or volunteers is in place.
❏	❏	3.6.2.3	The coordinator shall implement policies and procedures as recommended by the governing body.

Standard 3.6.3: Standards for Volunteers

Standard 3.6.3A: *Training and Development*

STANDARD: All volunteers are adequately trained to enable them to exhibit a high degree of volunteer professionalism. In addition, volunteers are acknowledged for their valuable contributions.

RATIONALE: To ensure the quality of AAA/AAT, an ongoing training, education, and recognition/appreciation plan for volunteers is provided. This will also reduce liability and provide for the well-being of all participants, including clients, visitors, volunteers, staff, and animals.

Meets Criterion	Needs Attention	Criteria	
❏	❏	3.6.3A.1	The AAA/AAT provider shall have an appointed training coordinator for volunteers.
❏	❏	3.6.3A.2	There shall be information on file about each volunteer's background, interests, training, program involvement, and performance.
❏	❏	3.6.3A.3	Volunteers shall provide a written description of volunteer responsibilities (job description), and volunteer and program policies. Policies shall include emergency procedures, clear reporting guidelines, and a program/organization mission statement.

Meets Criterion	Needs Attention	Criteria	
❏	❏	3.6.3A.4	Initial orientation and continuing education shall be provided to all volunteer personnel.
❏	❏	3.6.3A.5	Pertinent program resource materials shall be provided to volunteers. Resource materials shall include information on various animal species, their behaviors and needs, the facilities visited, and client populations.
❏	❏	3.6.3A.6	Volunteers shall receive training about potential risks to animals or themselves and techniques for reducing risks.
❏	❏	3.6.3A.7	Continuing education/in-service training shall be provided to volunteers. Training shall focus on facility procedures, activity/treatment goals, and clientele.
❏	❏	3.6.3A.8	Recognition/appreciation shall be provided for volunteer teams' valuable contributions.

Standard 3.6.4: Volunteer Agreements

STANDARD: Written volunteer agreements regarding important expectations are provided. These agreements are completed and signed by the volunteer prior to beginning service.

RATIONALE: In order to work most effectively, volunteers must understand acceptable performance standards. The provider and/or facility shall provide a written volunteer agreement to inform all volunteers of what is expected.

Meets Criterion	Needs Attention	Criteria	
❏	❏	3.6.4.1	A written volunteer agreement, understood and signed by the volunteer, is provided prior to participation.
❏	❏	3.6.4.2	The volunteer agreement shall include the volunteer's general responsibilities.

Meets Criterion	Needs Attention	Criteria	
❏	❏	3.6.4.3	The volunteer agreement shall include an expectation about providing accurate documentation on a volunteer application, visit summaries, and incident reports.
❏	❏	3.6.4.4	The volunteer agreement shall include a policy regarding humane treatment of animals.
❏	❏	3.6.4.5	The volunteer agreement shall include written expectations about appropriate treatment of program participants.
❏	❏	3.6.4.6	The volunteer agreement shall include expectations about attendance and punctuality.
❏	❏	3.6.4.7	Volunteers shall meet the health and legal requirements (e.g., TB test, criminal background check, etc.) of the facilities in which they work.

Standard 3.7: Standards for Performance Evaluations

Standard 3.7.1: Performance Evaluation Policies and Procedures

STANDARD: All program personnel, whether volunteer or paid, receive regular written performance evaluations based on job descriptions and responsibilities.

RATIONALE: To ensure program quality, personnel deserve to receive regular information about their job performance. Performance evaluations provide for continuing quality improvement and are designed to provide positive feedback as well as corrective information.

Meets Criterion	Needs Attention	Criteria	
❏	❏	3.7.1.1	The program shall use a standard format to provide written performance evaluations to all program personnel.

Meets Criterion	Needs Attention	Criteria	
❑	❑	3.7.1.2	The program shall have a written policy for all personnel which defines minimum performance requirements for continued participation in the program.
❑	❑	3.7.1.3	The program coordinator or designee shall complete performance evaluations after observing personnel interact with clients and/or other staff
❑	❑	3.7.1.4	New personnel shall receive an initial performance evaluation at the completion of a probationary period.
❑	❑	3.7.1.5	The program shall conduct performance evaluations on a regular basis at an interval not to exceed one year.

Standard 3.7.2: AAA/AAT Specialist Evaluation

STANDARD: AAA/AAT Specialists are evaluated on a regular schedule regarding professional competence and the provision of AAA/AAT services.

RATIONALE: To encourage professional growth and improve performance, the provider and/or individual needs regular evaluation of AAA/AAT services. Evaluation shall be based on client outcome criteria identified at the beginning of services being rendered.

Meets Criterion	Needs Attention	Criteria	
❑	❑	3.7.2.1	Evaluations shall be based on outcome criteria identified at the beginning of services, utilizing a standard format.
❑	❑	3.7.2.2	Evaluation reports shall be maintained by the supervisor or agency contracting for AAA/AAT services.
❑	❑	3.7.2.3	Evaluations shall address both field of practice and incorporation of AAA/AAT.

Meets Criterion	Needs Attention	Criteria	
❑	❑	3.7.2.4	Original copies of performance evaluations shall be kept in the AAA/AAT Specialist's personnel record.

Standard 3.7.3: Volunteer Evaluation

STANDARD: The program has a written volunteer performance evaluation policy and procedure plan that is based on the volunteer agreement and job description, and which is provided to the volunteer.

RATIONALE: To ensure that volunteers are meeting program expectations adequately, a volunteer performance evaluation plan is written, adhered to, and reviewed on a regular basis.

Meets Criterion	Needs Attention	Criteria	
❑	❑	3.7.3.3	Volunteers shall be evaluated for their ability to meet program goals.
❑	❑	3.7.3.2	Evaluation criteria shall be based on the volunteer agreement and/or job description.
❑	❑	3.7.3.3	Volunteers shall be made aware of the performance evaluation plan, and the coordinator or designee shall conduct evaluations in accordance with this plan.
❑	❑	3.7.3.4	The performance evaluation plan shall include written procedures to provide for redirecting volunteers whose performance is outside the acceptable standard. Redirection shall be progressive and shall include such procedures as counseling, reassignment, administrative leave, or dismissal when appropriate.
❑	❑	3.7.3.5	Volunteers shall receive performance evaluations on a regular basis, at an interval not to exceed one year.

Meets Criterion	Needs Attention	Criteria	
❏	❏	3.7.3.6	The coordinator or facility liaison shall review the volunteers performance evaluation with the volunteer in person.
❏	❏	3.7.3.6	The provider organization/provider program provides contingency planning procedures for emergencies and unplanned incidents.

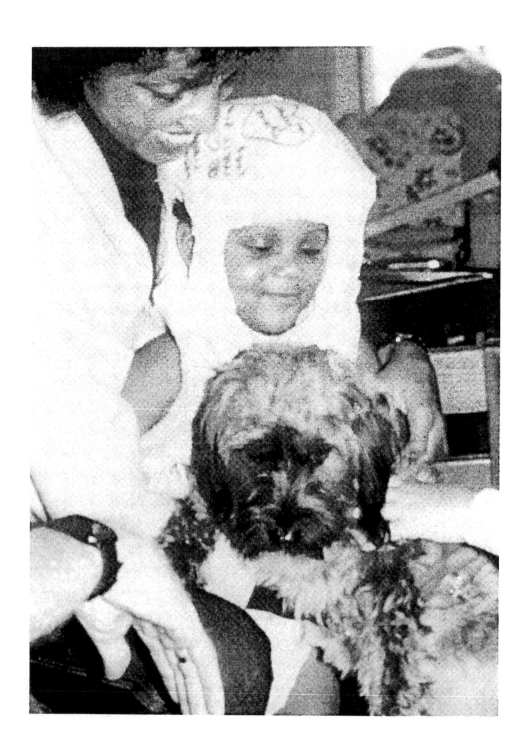

Animal-Assisted Therapy—An Animal-Assisted Therapy Specialist (Physical Therapist) works with a child and dog to improve upper body strength. The dog did not
need to know specialized commands in order to provide motivation for this young
child. *(Photo courtesy of Denver Children's Hospital, Denver, CO.)*

Section 4: Standards for Service Delivery

The integration of animals, handlers, staff, and clients is the central challenge to the success of AAA/AAT. Given the diversity of settings, animals and clients involved in AAA/AAT, it is difficult to provide one set of guidelines that will cover the needs of all. This section addresses considerations common to the practice of AAA/AAT across the spectrum.

Includes:

4.1	Standards for Client Assessment
4.2	Standards for Goals and Objectives
	4.2A Standards for AAA Plans
	4.2B Standards for AAT Plans
4.3	Standards for Service Documentation
	4.3A Standards for AAA Documentation
	4.3B Standards for AAT Documentation
4.5	Standards for Client Rights
4.6	Standards for Confidentiality
4.7	Standards for Infection Control
4.8	Standards for Incident Reports

Standard 4.1: Standards for Client Assessment

STANDARD: A specific method for identifying appropriate AAA/AAT clients is developed and implemented.

RATIONALE: Applied client assessment procedures help ensure the development of effective, goal-oriented care plans and the successful matching of clients with animals.

Meets Criterion	Needs Attention	Criteria	
❑	❑	4.1.1	Assessment procedures shall identify facility dynamics, including facility activity, potential distractions, and predictability of client behavior and how these factors impact human-animal interactions.

Meets Criterion	Needs Attention	Criteria	
☐	☐	4.1.2	Assessment procedures shall identify animal handler experience level in AAA/AAT.
☐	☐	4.1.3	Assessment procedures shall identify number and skills of staff members involved in human-animal interactions.
☐	☐	4.1.4	Assessment procedures shall identify animal aptitude and skills required for AAA/AAT.
☐	☐	4.1.5	Assessment procedures shall identify factors affecting client suitability for AAA/AAT including allergies, phobias or fears, behavioral or medical contra-indications, and potential for harming animals.
☐	☐	4.1.6	The assessment shall specify recommendations for client participation in AAA/AAT.
☐	☐	4.1.7	A plan for ongoing client assessment shall be provided.

Standard 4.2: Standards for Goals and Objectives

STANDARD: Clear goals and objectives exist prior to implementation of AAA/AAT services. Goals and objectives are measurable. The AAA/AAT services are structured and administered to achieve its stated, measurable goals and objectives.

RATIONALE: Clearly stated goals and objectives provide essential direction for AAA/AAT implementation and provide a method to measure performance in specific areas of client functioning or services. Measurable goals and objectives assist in documenting the impact of AAA/AAT which may be necessary to justify services, costs, expansion, third party reimbursement, as well as to assist in investigative studies.

Meets Criterion	Needs Attention	Criteria	
☐	☐	4.2.1	Written goals and objectives for AAA/AAT services are based on the identified needs of the client population(s), or individual.

Meets Criterion	Needs Attention	Criteria	
❏	❏	4.2.2	AAA/AAT providers shall show written evidence that AAA/AAT goals and objectives are met.
❏	❏	4.2.3	The facility may require written evidence that client AAA/AAT goals and objectives are evaluated and documented.

Standard 4.2A: Standards for AAA Plans

STANDARD: Activity plans are developed for all clients receiving AAA services.

RATIONALE: Activity plans enable providers to design sessions that ensure appropriate incorporation of animals. Formal plans provide accountability for personnel and provide a means to measure client change. Familiarity with activity plans allows those who interact with clients to impact clients in a beneficial manner.

Meets Criterion	Needs Attention	Criteria	
❏	❏	4.2A.1	The activity plan is developed with the assistance of an AAA Specialist.
❏	❏	4.2A.2	The activity plan shall provide specific assessment of facility dynamics, animal skills and aptitude, and animal handler skills to match animals with clients.
❏	❏	4.2A.3	The activity plan shall identify the methods to be used to accomplish stated activity plan goals.
❏	❏	4.2A.4	The activity plan shall provide procedures for re-evaluation, modification, and adaptation of activities.
❏	❏	4.2A.5	The activity plan shall identify criteria to evaluate achievement of stated objectives and goals.

Standard 4.2B: Standards for AAT Plans

STANDARD: A treatment plan is provided for clients receiving AAT services.

RATIONALE: Individualized treatment/education plans enable providers to design sessions that address specified client goals and ways animals are incorporated. Formal plans provide accountability for personnel and provide a means to measure client change. Familiarity with treatment/education plans allows those who interact with clients to impact them in a beneficial manner.

Meets Criterion	Needs Attention	Criteria	
❑	❑	4.2B.1	The treatment/education plan is delivered or directed by an AAA Specialist within the scope of her profession.
❑	❑	4.2B.1	The treatment/education plan shall provide specific assessment of facility dynamics, animal skills and aptitude, and animal handler skills to match animals with clients.
❑	❑	4.2B.2	The treatment/education plan shall identify short- and long-term measurable goals and objectives for each participating client, as appropriate.
❑	❑	4.2B.3	The treatment/education plan shall identify the methodologies to be used to accomplish stated treatment/education plan goals.
❑	❑	4.2B.4	The treatment/education plan shall provide procedures for re-evaluation, modification, and adaptation of client interventions.
❑	❑	4.2B.5	The treatment/education plan shall identify criteria to evaluate achievement by individual clients of stated objectives and goals.
❑	❑	4.2B.1	The treatment/education plan is reviewed and evaluated by a AAT Specialist within the scope of his or her profession.

Standard 4.3: **Service Documentation**

STANDARD: Documentation of AAA/AAT services is maintained.

RATIONALE: To ensure service quality, enhance credibility, provide statistical information, and address liability concerns, the provider maintains documentation covering all aspects of AAA/AAT services. This provides the means for ongoing assessment to better meet the needs of the clients as well as the needs of the facility. Documentation helps to build credibility, increase professionalism, and provides a data base for investigative studies.

Meets Criterion	Needs Attention	Criteria	
❏	❏	4.3.1	Providers shall complete visiting animal documentation forms after each visit and shall include information on date and time of visit, provider(s) and animal(s) involved, facility and population served, the interaction, and any incidents that occur.
❏	❏	4.3.2	Documentation forms or copies shall be made available to providers upon request, as appropriate.
❏	❏	4.3.3	All documentation forms completed by providers shall be reviewed and revised by the coordinator or designee on a regular basis.

Standard 4.3A: Standards for AAA Documentation

STANDARD: Documentation reflects the goals and objectives of AAA and includes client progress notes appropriate to the standard of the professional's licensing body.

RATIONALE: Complete activity documentation ensures a plan that measures client progress and answers legal accountability issues.

Meets Criterion	Needs Attention	Criteria	
❏	❏	4.3A.1	A description of the client shall always be included in documentation.

Meets Criterion	Needs Attention	Criteria	
❏	❏	4.3A.2	Observations, incidents, and progress shall be noted, including resolutions and follow-up.
❏	❏	4.3A.3	Data collected for investigative studies shall be properly authorized and managed.

Standard 4.3B: Standards for AAT Documentation

STANDARD: Documentation reflects the specific AAT goals and objectives and includes client progress notes appropriate to the standard of the education/human service provider's licensing body.

RATIONALE: To ensure a plan to measure client progress and to answer issues of legal accountability, as well as to adhere to goals and objectives and program assessment, the health/human service provider completes service documentation that meets the standards of his/her own licensing body.

Meets Criterion	Needs Attention	Criteria	
❏	❏	4.3B.1	A description of the client shall always be included in documentation.
❏	❏	4.3B.2	All entries shall be dated and signed by the service provider.
❏	❏	4.3B.3	All entries shall be made in ink.
❏	❏	4.3B.4	All plans (i.e., education and treatment) shall be filed and retrievable.
❏	❏	4.3B.5	Observations, incidents, and progress shall be noted, including resolutions and follow up.
❏	❏	4.3B.6	Data collected for investigative studies shall be properly authorized and managed.
❏	❏	4.3B.7	Documentation shall be kept for the period of time regulated by statute, but for a minimum of three years.

Meets Criterion	Needs Attention	Criteria	
❑	❑	4.3B.8	Treatment/education plans specify the strengths and needs of the client, goals and objectives of intervention, modality, and type of AAT services to be provided.
❑	❑	4.3B.9	Treatment/education plans are based upon a persisting complaint or problem, needs of the client, and the desired outcome.
❑	❑	4.3B.10	Treatment/education plans are reviewed by an AAT Specialist.

Standard 4.4: **Client Rights**

STANDARD: The rights of clients are recognized and respected at all times.

RATIONALE: A beneficial aspect of AAA/AAT programs is directly dependent upon the positive perceptions of the clients. Individual clients' rights must be respected.

Meets Criterion	Needs Attention	Criteria	
❑	❑	4.4.1	The needs and rights of all clients, including those who may be present but are not participating in the AAA/AAT program, are identified.

Standard 4.5: **Confidentiality**

STANDARD: Personnel involved in AAA/AAT adhere to practices that ensure client confidentiality.

RATIONALE: Personnel must guard and respect the dignity, privacy, and anonymity of clients participating in AAA/AAT services. Such personnel shall carefully plan and monitor this intimate, trusting relationship.

Meets Criterion	Needs Attention	Criteria	
❑	❑	4.5.1	All personnel, whether paid or volunteer, shall understand, sign an agreement concerning, and abide by program and/or facility confidentiality policies.
❑	❑	4.5.2	Signed confidentiality forms shall be maintained at the appropriate site.
❑	❑	4.5.3	The importance and terms of clients' rights and confidentiality shall be stressed at the provider and facility level.
❑	❑	4.5.4	The provider and/or the facility shall have a designated manager (i.e., a team leader and/or facility liaison) who shall be responsible for monitoring and ensuring that the terms of the confidentiality statement are met.
❑	❑	4.5.5	All signed confidentiality records and documents shall be filed for a minimum of three years and shall be kept in an identified, accessible location.

Standard 4.6: **Infection Control**

STANDARD: Written protocols are provided by each facility receiving services, to address infection control, including public safety, welfare, and zoonotic disease concerns.

RATIONALE: To assure that AAA/AAT represents limited risk to public health and safety, written instructions about infection control concerns, procedures associated with animal contact, and appropriate documentation are maintained.

Meets Criterion	Needs Attention	Criteria	
❑	❑	4.6.1	Written protocols detailing infection control procedures are maintained and adhered to.
❑	❑	4.6.2	The infection control protocol shall address public health and safety, and zoonotic disease concerns.

Meets Criterion	Needs Attention	Criteria	
❑	❑	4.6.3	Infection control protocol shall be designed to meet the needs of the client population.
❑	❑	4.6.4	Special consideration shall be given to infection control protocols for immune-compromised and/or pregnant populations.
❑	❑	4.6.5	Records of animal health screenings shall be maintained by the animal handler.

Standard 4.7: **Incident Reports**

STANDARD: Policies and procedures will be provided for reporting incidents between animals and people that may directly or indirectly affect AAA/AAT services.

RATIONALE: Human-animal interaction carries the potential for real or perceived injury. Documentation of incidents which affect perception of public health and safety is critical to ensure AAA/AAT viability.

Meets Criterion	Needs Attention	Criteria	
❑	❑	4.7.1	All personnel involved in AAA/AAT shall be provided with written procedures for documenting instances of accident or unusual occurrence.
❑	❑	4.7.2	Personnel shall report instances of accident or unusual occurrence to credentialling organizations withing 24 hours.
❑	❑	4.7.3	A procedure shall be provided for client and collateral staff or witness(es) to document their observation of the accident or unusual occurrence.
❑	❑	4.7.4	Animals shall be reassessed in instances that may directly or indirectly affect AAA/AAT.
❑	❑	4.7.5	*Inappropriate interactions* are defined, and a plan for disengagement procedures, remedial action, and reporting is maintained.

Meets Criterion	Needs Attention	Criteria	
❑	❑	4.7.6	The provider shall report to credentialing organization potentially harmful or dangerous interactions or behaviors (on the part of people or animals) including incidents causing, or with potential to cause, injury or upset to animals or people.
❑	❑	4.7.7	The provider shall request that the facility identify and describe client behaviors which may endanger other individuals and/or animals.
❑	❑	4.7.8	The provider shall request that the facility provide specific procedures for dealing with inappropriate behaviors by clients.

Section 5: Standards for Animals

Animals involved in AAA/AAT are specifically selected, trained, and in excellent health in order to participate effectively and safely. This section focuses on the specific requirements of animals.

Includes:

5.1	Standards for Animal Selection
5.2	Standards for Animal Health and Management
5.3	Standards for Animal Husbandry
5.4	Standards for Veterinary Input

Standard 5.1: Selection

STANDARD: Animals that participate in Animal-Assisted Activities/Animal-Assisted Therapy (AAA/AAT) are purposefully selected, healthy, and meet risk management criteria. They meet the aptitude, size, age, and skill level required for their participation to be beneficial.

RATIONALE: Selection standards identify those animals that are reliable, controllable, predictable, and suitable to the particular AAA/AAT task, population, and working environment. Species, breed type, sex, age, size, health, aptitude, suitability are all factors that impact the success of animal-assisted interactions. Consideration of these factors will minimize risk for animals and people.

Meets Criterion	Needs Attention	Criteria	
❏	❏	5.1.1	**Reliability:** The provider shall provide a documented history of the animals' reaction to a variety of social contexts, based on prolonged interaction between the animal and handler.
❏	❏	5.1.2	**Reliability:** The provider shall provide information on any incidents involving animals which may directly or indirectly affect public health and safety.

Meets Criterion	Needs Attention	Criteria	
❑	❑	5.1.3	**Controllability:** The provider shall provide documentation that demonstrates that the animal can be directed and engaged or disengaged from interactions or tasks easily in a manner which inspires confidence in clients and staff. Clients must perceive that their safety is assured.
❑	❑	5.1.4	**Predictability:** The provider shall provide documentation indicating the animal demonstrates acceptable behavior during task-appropriate simulations of AAA/AAT situations and as observed on site by staff.
❑	❑	5.1.5	**Suitability:** The provider shall take into account age, sex, size, type, and breed/species-typical behaviors when matching animals with specific client populations and tasks.
❑	❑	5.1.6	**Suitability:** The provider shall ensure a suitable match between client needs and environmental dynamics, animal skills and aptitude, and handler knowledge, skills, and experience.

Standard 5.2:   **Health and Management**

STANDARD: Health and management practices help to maintain optimal animal health and well-being through appropriate hygiene, management, specific preventative care, and prompt attention to illness. Training and handling methods and the equipment incorporated must be humane. It is unacceptable to use drugs or other means to chemically alter the animal's behavior.

RATIONALE: In order for AAA/AAT interactions to be mutually beneficial, animals must be in optimum health. Maintaining good physical health and emotional well-being requires active animal management. Humane treatment of the animals is influenced by the public's perception of the training methods and equipment. This perception can directly affect the public's level of confidence in the handler and the animal.

Meets Criterion	Needs Attention	Criteria	
❏	❏	5.2.1	Documentation of annual vaccinations, rabies vaccinations, and other screening tests (e.g., fecal flotation examination) as advised by risk management policies shall be maintained by the provider or handler.
❏	❏	5.2.2	The animals participating in AAA/AAT shall be an appropriate weight based upon the animals' age, species, breed, type, and required level of exercise.
❏	❏	5.2.3	The provider shall provide continual evaluation of the effect of interactions with people in the facility on the animal's health and behavior (animal stress level).
❏	❏	5.2.4	Animal handlers shall utilize transportation procedures that consider the animal's well-being as the primary focus. Transportation criteria shall address preparation, acclimation, transport, and condition upon arrival.
❏	❏	5.2.5	Residential animals shall be provided housing that meets habitat, safety, welfare, and behavioral needs.
❏	❏	5.2.6	Animals shall be trained to a task-specific level that provides a sufficient means of communication to enable the handler to reliably direct the animal in a manner that is humane and inspires confidence in all team members.
❏	❏	5.2.7	Equipment such as collars, leashes, harnesses, etc. shall be appropriate to the animal and the task, be perceived as humane, and inspire confidence in the team as to reliability and safety. They shall fit correctly and be maintained in good condition.
❏	❏	5.2.8	Outdoor areas shall be designated for animal exercise and toileting. Appropriate clean-up procedures, tools, and receptacles shall be used.

Meets Criterion	Needs Attention	Criteria	
❏	❏	5.2.9	All animals working in AAA/AAT shall be treated with respect and in a responsible manner. Animals shall not be used in breeding programs for the purpose of supplying animals for additional programs or facilities.
❏	❏	5.2.10	Residential dogs and cats shall be spayed or neutered prior to entry into programs.
❏	❏	5.2.11	All dogs and cats shall be licensed in accordance with the requirements of local jurisdictions.
❏	❏	5.2.12	Exercise, rest, and relaxation shall be regularly scheduled for the animals.

Standard 5.3: **Husbandry**

STANDARD: The facility will specify procedures for maintaining a safe, clean, and healthful environment for people and animals.

RATIONALE: To reduce opportunities for zoonosis and to facilitate appropriate and beneficial interactions between people and animals involved in AAA/AAT, the needs of each must be adequately addressed.

Meets Criterion	Needs Attention	Criteria	
❏	❏	5.3.1	The facility shall provide written procedures for sanitation, designating locations for animal urination, defecation, feeding, watering, grooming, exercise, and housing.
❏	❏	5.3.2	A clean, safe environment shall be provided when the animal is not engaged in AAA/AAT.
❏	❏	5.3.3	The facility shall provide written procedures for periodic safety checks of animal housing, equipment and emergency procedures.

Meets Criterion	Needs Attention	Criteria	
❏	❏	5.3.4	The facility shall provide written procedures for appropriate disposal of animal wastes.

Standard 5.4: **Veterinary Input**

STANDARD: Screening and participation requirements include input from a veterinary professional skilled in working with the types of animals participating in AAA/AAT.

RATIONALE: Consultation with a veterinarian helps ensure that animal health and well-being are addressed in a knowledgeable and up-to-date manner.

Meets Criterion	Needs Attention	Criteria	
❏	❏	5.4.1	The veterinary professional shall be available for consultation as needed to support provider efforts and activities.
❏	❏	5.4.2	A veterinary professional shall contribute to the establishment of infection control procedures and education about zoonotic issues.
❏	❏	5.4.3	Consultation with a veterinary professional shall occur on a regular basis that is consistent with the needs of the animal, program, handler, and facility.

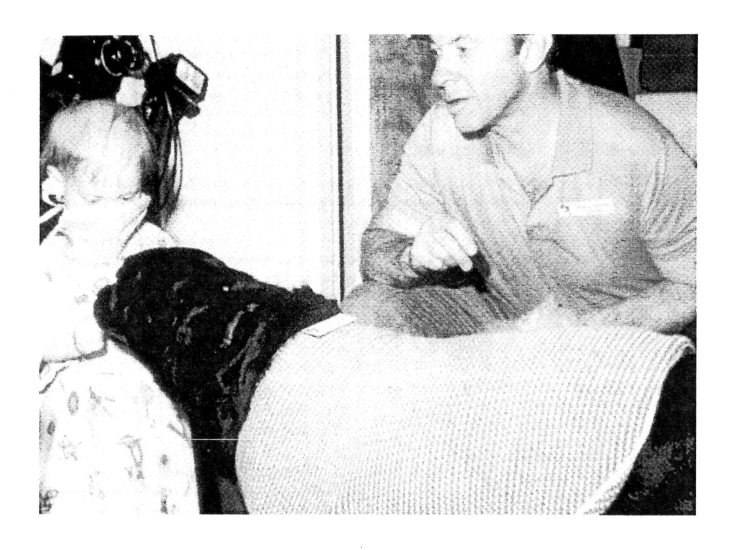

Animal-Assisted Activities—A good example of infection control precautions in use with client, dog and Volunteer Animal Handler. *(Photo courtesy of Denver Children's Hospital, Denver, CO.)*

Section 6: Standards for Investigative Studies

This section deals with concerns regarding research in the field of AAA/AAT.

Includes:

6.1   Investigative Studies

Standard 6.1: Investigative Studies

STANDARD: Procedures for the conduct of any investigative studies involving AAA/AAT are reviewed and approved by the appropriate personnel of the provider organizations and facilities involved..

RATIONALE: Investigative studies involving AAA/AAT comply with federally recognized standards and requirements. Investigative studies are needed to further knowledge and techniques in the field of AAA/AAT.

Meets Criterion	Needs Attention	Criteria	
❑	❑	6.1.1	Investigative study methodologies involving AAA/AAT programs shall be reviewed and approved by the receiving facility.
❑	❑	6.1.2	When there are no standards or requirements in place for AAA/AAT investigative studies, the principles of existing governmental policies shall be used as guidelines.
❑	❑	6.1.3	Investigative studies shall be conducted in compliance with all facility policies and governmental regulations involving human and animal subjects.
❑	❑	6.1.4	Written confidentiality criteria shall be established and adhered to in all investigative study efforts.
❑	❑	6.1.5	Investigative studies shall not cause undue stress to the people or animals involved.

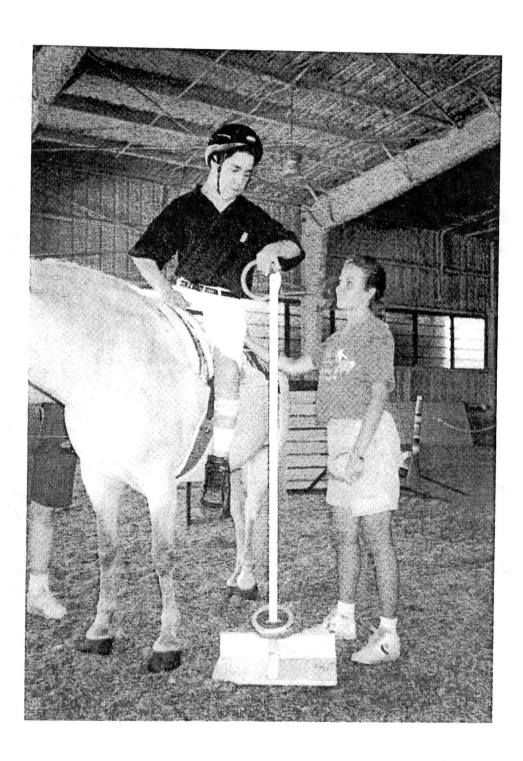

Animal-Assisted Therapy—An Animal-Assisted Therapy Specialist (Occupational Therapist) uses a horse to focus on motor, cognitive and affective skill development. Animal handler assists the therapist. *(Photo courtesy of Thorncroft Riding Program.)*

Appendix A: GUIDELINES FOR EDUCATIONAL CURRICULA

The following terms and definitions promote clear communication among persons involved in programs concerning human-animal interactions. Terms were identified to indicate whether a particular program or process involved therapy, therapeutic intervention or recognition of the importance of the human-animal bond. The definitions do not imply a hierarchy but a relational arrangement. Therefore, "Animal-Assisted Activities" is most inclusive while "Animal-Assisted Therapy" and "Human-Animal Support Services" are less so. Terms thought to be most inclusive were selected to provide the greatest flexibility with the definitions. Thus "animal" was selected as it is more inclusive than the term "pet." The term "assisted" was felt to indicate greater participation than "facilitated." Therefore, "animal-assisted" is preferred to "pet-facilitated."

Generic Terms and Definitions

Animal-Assisted Activities (AAA) provide opportunities for motivational, educational, and/or recreational, benefits to enhance quality of life. AAA are delivered in a variety of environments by a specially trained professional, paraprofessional, and/or volunteer in association with animals that meet specific criteria.

Animal-Assisted Therapy (AAT) is a goal directed intervention in which an animal meeting specific criteria is an integral part of the treatment process. AAT is delivered and/or directed by a health/human service provider working within the scope of her/his profession. AAT is designed to promote improvement in human physical, social, emotional, and/or cognitive functioning. AAT is provided in a variety of settings, and may be group or individual in nature. The process is documented and evaluated.

Human-Animal Support Services (HASS) enhance and encourage the responsible and humane interrelationship of people, animals, and nature.

Personnel

Animal-Assisted Activities (AAA)

A person who provides AAA possesses specialized knowledge of animals and the populations with which s/he interacts in delivering motivational, educational, and/or recreational animal-oriented activities. The individual may work independently when s/he has specialized training. Trained volunteers are often involved in AAA.

This may include but is not limited to such individuals as:

activity directors
animal health technicians
animal shelter workers
camp counselors
dog trainers
educators
licensed practical nurses
licensed vocational nurses
nature counselors

nursing assistants/aids
occupational therapy assistants
physical therapy assistants
recreation therapy aides
riding instructors
student nurses
trained volunteers
visiting pet specialists
4-H leaders

Animal-Assisted Therapy (AAT)

The professional who delivers and/or directs Animal-Assisted Therapy (AAT) is a health/human service provider with expertise in incorporating animals as a treatment modality, and is knowledgeable about animals. The AAT Specialist is licensed and/or recognized by a separate professional discipline. This individual complies with the legal and ethical requirements of his/her profession; as well as local, state and federal laws relating to this work.

This may include but is not limited to such individuals as:

certified alcoholism counselors
licensed counselors
marriage, family and child counselors
occupational therapists
recreational therapists
registered nurses
physicians
psychologists
vocational rehabilitation counselors

speech pathologists
speech therapists
social workers
pastoral counselors
physical therapists
school counselors
special education counselors
psychotherapists

Human-Animal Support Services (HASS)

A person who provides HASS may be a professional, paraprofessional or trained volunteer working within the legal and ethical scope of his/her job description or practice. These services target support to the pet/animal owner.

This might include but is not limited to such individuals as:

animal behaviorists

animal trainers

grief counselors

trained volunteers

K-9 Units: army/police, or rescue

pet fostering

pet loss counselors

self-help coordinators

veterinarians

AAA Specialists...

Manage AAA Program

- Administer AAA Programs
- Participate in fund-raising
- Determine fiscal impact of AAA and fiscally manage AAA Program
- Recruit, train, supervise, and evaluate AAA volunteers and staff
- Introduce AAA to institutions and interrelate AAA as a benefit to client health and well-being
- Write and interpret policies

Interface with the Team

- Provide and/or receive referrals
- Exhibit strong interpersonal skills
- Professionalism
- Meet and maintain minimal requirements for professional licensing and certification in original field
- Networking

Provide Recommendations Related to Incorporation of AAA

- Demonstrate knowledge of different applications and techniques
- Demonstrate knowledge of interaction techniques

Incorporate Animals in Activities

- Select animals according to:
  —health requirements
  —aptitude evaluation
  —skills demonstration
  —behavioral requirements
  —animal's ability to cope with stress
- Determine appropriate placement through:
  —response to people
  —response to other animals
  —risk

- Provide or direct animal care to include:
  —training
  —maintain health requirements and veterinary care
  —appropriate diet
  —adequate exercise
  —use of appropriate products and supplies
  —stress reduction techniques
  —working with animals
  —ensure appropriate training and handling of animals
  —identify and train basic skills required of animals
  —identify and train advanced skills to enhance interactions
- Demonstrate background knowledge to include:
  —zoonoses
  —animal aptitude
  —animal behavior
  —animal stressors and stress-related behaviors
  —animal care, to include the use of appropriate products
  —equipment needs, uses, and contraindications
  —understanding human/animal interactions
  —identifying need for and properly initiating a new animal into AAA
  —identifying need for and properly terminating an animal's participation in AAA
  —the relationships between animal and human abuse
  —knowledge of human life-cycle

Advocate AAA

- Provide information on AAA to include:
  —the role of pets in the family
  —therapeutic effects of animals
  —applications of AAA
- Referral
- Resources
- Networking
- Distinction between therapy animals and service animals

Animal-Assisted Activities Specialist
DUTIES

| **Program Planning** | Develop/Prioritize Goals and Objectives | Develop Policies/ Procedures | Conduct Needs Assessment |
| | Develop Programs | Coordinate Community Resources | Develop Team-Building Programs |

| **Program Management** | Maintain Records | Evaluate Programs | Conduct Program Activities |

| **Volunteer/Staff Management** | Recruit Volunteers/Staff | Assign Volunteers/ Staff Appropriately | Provide Supplies/ Equipment |

| **Animal Management** | Select/Screen Animals | Register/Provide Identification | Train Animals |
| | Practice Safety | | |

| **Training and Education** | Develop/Revise Volunteer Handbook | Develop Age-Appropriate Programs | Comply with State Education Requirements |

| **Public Relations** | Conduct Program Promotion | Develop Support Information | Network with Other Programs |

| **Professional Development** | Comply with Professional/Humane Ethics | Maintain Professional Certification | Network with Peers |

Evaluate Facility	Obtain Administrative Approval	Provide Budget Planning	Identify/Meet Insurance/ Liability Needs
Communicate Effectively	Implement Forms		
Provide Problem Management	Evaluate Program Performance	Offer Support Groups	
Provide Equipment	Apply Knowledge of Animal Behavior	Schedule Regular Veterinary Care	Provide Care of Animals
Develop Training Sessions	Conduct In-Service Training	Serve as Community Resource	Involve Interns and Education Programs
Collaborate with Government Agencies	Develop Special Events	Maintain Information Referral System	Conduct Public Speaking/Lectures
Maintain Professional Memberships	Maintain Knowledge of Relevant Literature	Publish Professional Articles	

AAT Specialists...

Manage AAT Program

- Administer AAT Programs
- Participate in fund-raising
- Determine fiscal impact of AAT and fiscally manage AAT Program
- Recruit, train, supervise, and evaluate AAT volunteers and staff
- Introducing AAT to treatment institutions and interrelating AAT as a treatment modality
- Write and interpret policies

Perform Program Evaluations

- Develop and implement observation/data collection techniques
- Develop and implement evaluation procedures
- Pet preference
- Pet history
- Knowledge of appropriate measures, which may include:
  — bonding scales
  — Poretsky scales
  — empathy scales
  — anxiety scales
  — depression scales
  — physical improvement measures
- Knowledge of where to find resources and ability to survey literature

Interface with the Team

- Provide and/or receive referrals
- Exhibit strong interpersonal skills
- Demonstrate and implement collaboration and teaming with other specialties, volunteers, etc.
- Professionalism
- Meet and maintain minimal requirements for professional licensing and certification in original field
- Networking

Provide Diagnosis Related to Incorporation of AAT

- Demonstrate knowledge of different applications and techniques
- Demonstrate knowledge of interactive therapies
- Incorporate different methods of treatment
- Demonstrate humane animal handling skills

Provide Prescription Related to AAT

- Assess client needs
- Determine individualized client goals
- Assess client appropriateness for AAT
- Determine contraindications for AAT
- Write treatment plan
- Implement treatment plan
- Evaluate client progress
- Evaluate effectiveness of AAT in meeting client goals

Incorporate Animals in Treatment

- Animal selection process includes:
  — health requirements
  — aptitude evaluation
  — skills demonstration
  — animal behavior
  — animal stress
- Determine appropriate placement through:
  — response to people
  — response to other animals
  — liability
- Provide or direct animal care to include:
  — training
  — maintain health requirements and veterinary care
  — appropriate diet
  — adequate exercise
  — use of appropriate products and supplies
  — stress reduction techniques
- Working with Animals
- Assure appropriate training and handling of animals
- Identify and train basic skills required of the animals

- Identify and train advanced skills to enhance interactions
- Demonstrate knowledge of:
  — zoonoses
  — animal aptitude
  — animal behavior
  — animal stressors and stress-related behaviors
- Demonstrate knowledge of animal care, to include the use of appropriate products
- Demonstrate knowledge of equipment needs, uses, and contraindications
- Understanding human/animal interactions
- Identify need for and properly initiate a new animal into AAT
- Identify need for and properly terminate an animal's participation in AAT
- Demonstrate background knowledge to include:
  — role of the pet in the family
  — evolution and historical development of human/animal relations
  — role of nature and animals in modern life
  — the relationship between animal abuse and child abuse
  — knowledge of life-cycle
  — behavior
  — communication
  — understanding of ecosystem
  — interspecies interactions
  — therapeutic and educational uses of animals

Interface with the Community

- Provide information to the public
- Provide public education presentations

Risk Management Practices

- Develop, implement, evaluate, and revise policies to include:
  — zoonotic concerns and prevention measures
  — infection control concerns and prevention measures
  — liability concerns and prevention measures
- Demonstrate handling and interaction techniques that reduce risks
- Maintain health requirements for animals and handlers

Advocate AAT

- Provide information on AAT to include:
  — the role of pets in the family
  — therapeutic effects of animals
  — applications of AAT
  — the relationship between animal abuse and child abuse
- Referral
- Resources
- Networking
- Public interaction on AAT issues
- Change the perception of animals in facilities
- Distinction between therapy animals and service animals

Animal-Assisted Therapy Specialist
DUTIES

Administration	Maintain Required Records	Manage Program	Conduct Short/Long Term Planning
	Develop New Programs	Maintain Supplies and Equipment	Interface with Admin./Volunteers
Quality/Risk Management Infection Control	Conduct Program Evaluation	Maintain Infection/Quality Control Protocols	Monitor Human-Animal Stress
	Maintain Emergency Procedures	Review Client Records	Collect Data
Client Services	Assess Client Appropriateness	Develop Treatment Plan	Define Role of Animal in Treatment
	Coordinate Collateral Support	Supervise Client Participation	Match Client with Animal
Volunteer Management	Develop Volunteer Training Requirements	Develop Training Materials	Conduct Volunteer Evaluations
	Monitor Volunteer and Animal Interactions	Facilitate Volunteer Termination	
Animal Management	Develop Policies/ Protocols for Animal Interactions	Recommend Animal Training Requirements	Maintain Mutually Beneficial Environment
Outreach	Assess Community Needs	Develop and Maintain Public Relations	Provide Community Education
Staff Relations	Provide Staff Training	Evaluate Staff	Supervise Staff
Professional Development	Maintain Professional Credentials/Licensure	Maintain Professional Insurance	Participate in Professional Organizations

Administer Program/ Policy Procedures	Assess/Evaluate Program Facilities	Maintain Budget	Write Funding Proposals
Ensure Ethical Standards	Provide Student Internship Opportunities		
Maintain Environmental Standards	Maintain Policies/ Procedures	Maintain Program Compliance	Monitor Volunteer Insurance Needs

Evaluate Treatment Process	Participate in Team Meetings	Documentation	Advocate for Clients
Provide Client Orientation	Execute Treatment Sessions	Facilitate Treatment Termination	
Train Volunteers	Recruit Volunteers	Manage Volunteers	Supervise Volunteers

Determine Animal Suitability	Supervise Animal Care	Maintain Animal Credentials
Develop/Implement Marketing Plan	Develop and Maintain Media Resources	Provide Consulting Services
Coordinate Staff	Monitor Staff Workload	Assess and Maintain Staff Client Ratio
Maintain Professional Decorum	Maintain Knowledge of Species/Breeds and Behaviors	Participate in Research

Standards of Practice for AAA/AAT

Appendix B: **SAMPLE FORMS**

Facility Confidentiality Agreement

As a protective measure for the privacy of our patients, we ask that each volunteer sign this confidentiality agreement:

I,_____ (print Volunteer's name), understand that in the course of my volunteer work I may be exposed to information of a confidential nature pertaining to patients and/or their families.

I will consider as confidential all information which I may hear directly or indirectly. I will not seek information in regard to a patient, except as it pertains to my volunteer assignment. I will not release information about patients or their families.

I will uphold the standards of this facility and will safeguard its reputation by maintaining the highest standard of confidentiality.

_____   _____
Volunteer's Signature   Date

_____   _____
Employee witness' Signature   Date

Visit Report

Facility: _____ Date: _____

Handlers Name: _____

Animal's Name and Species: _____

Approximate Number of Participants: _____
(include clients, visitors, and staff)

How did the Client(s) respond to the visit?
(What stands out about this visit?)

Were there any negative experiences?
(Please explain)

What was the setting like ?
(Where did you meet? Were clients up or in bed? Were staff present and helpful?)

How did your animal companion react?
(Nervous? Calm?)

What are your suggestions for future visits?

_____
Volunteer's Signature

Adapted with permission from *Caring Critters,* June 1992.

Incident Report Form

Date of Incident: _____ Time: _____

Place of Incident: _____ Client: _____

Therapist: _____ Volunteer: _____

Witness(es): _____

Animal's Name: _____ Species: _____

How did the incident happen?   (Who, What, When, Where, Why, How?)

Was anyone hurt? (circle one)   Yes   No
Describe the nature of the injury:

Was first aid given? (circle one)   Yes   No
Describe the first aid given:

Did the person who was injured resume his/her activities?   Yes   No
If No, please explain:

Was further medical treatment required?   Yes   No

Did/does client need to consult with a doctor?   Yes   No

_____   _____
Volunteer's Signature   Injured's Signature

_____   _____
AAA/T Coordinator's Signature   Witness' Signature

Adapted with permission from *National Capital Therapy Dogs, Inc.*, June 1992.

Facility Assessment Form

AAA/AAT

Section 1:   Facility Information

Facility Name: _____ Date: _____

Address: _____

Contact Name: _____

Telephone: _____ Title: _____

Funding Source: _____

Additional Staff Supporters: _____

Section 2:   Physical Space

Size: _____ Number of Rooms   _____ No. of Square Feet Per Room

Layout: _____ Number of Floors   _____ Common Areas

Floor Plan: On back of form draw room size, including furniture location.

Describe Access to Outdoors: _____

Describe Client Access to Outdoors: _____

List three to four attributes of the facility:

1) _____   2) _____

3) _____   4) _____

List three to four disadvantages of the facility:

1) _____   2) _____

3) _____   4) _____

Section 3:   Administration/Policies

Mission of the facility: _____

Administrative attitude: _____

_____

Health Department regulations: _____

_____

Existing infection control policies: _____

_____

Organizational needs: _____

_____

Section 4:   Staff

Staff/Client ratio: _____

Will program be documented? (Circle one)   Yes / No

Attach sample documentation form.

Who will do documentation? _____

Staff workload: (Circle one)   Low / Medium / High / Frantic / Census Varies Considerably

Interest in new programs: (Circle one) Extremely Low / Low / Medium / High

Which allied health professionals support program? _____

_____

Attach summary sheet of results of Animal Preference Questionnaire.

Section 5:   Environmental Concerns

Room arrangements: _____

Best time(s) for program: _____

Worst time(s) for program: _____

Traits of facility: _____

Other notes: _____

_____

Section 6:   Prioritizing Needs

List three to four criteria from each Section you want for an *ideal* program:

1) _____   2) _____

3) _____   4) _____

List three to four criteria from each Section you do *not* want:

1) _____   2) _____

3) _____   4) _____

List three to four criteria you *must* have for a successful program:

1) _____   2) _____

3) _____   4) _____

List three to four criteria that are not perfect but *can be* worked around:

1) _____   2) _____

3) _____   4) _____

DELTA SOCIETY, 1995.

Animal Preference Questionaire

Name (optional): _____ Date: _____

Title or Department Name: _____

Please check all that apply. If you have any comments, suggestions, or questions that are not addressed in this questionnaire, please feel free to write on the back of this sheet.

What is your opinion of the proposed plan to have selected animals visit this facility for clients to interact with?

_____ 1. Strongly Approve   _____ 4. Disapprove

_____ 2. Approve   _____ 5. Strongly Disapprove

_____ 3. Neither Approve nor Disapprove   _____ 6. No Opinion

Have you ever had a pet or pets?

_____ No, I have never had a pet.   _____ Yes. I have had a pet.

If yes, what kind(s) of pets have you had? _____

Do you have allergies to cats, dogs, or other animals?

_____ 1. No, I have no allergies to any animal as far as I know.

_____ 2. Yes, I am allergic to cats.

_____ 3. Yes, I am allergic to dogs.

_____ 4. Yes, I am allergic to the following animals: _____

Do you dislike or are you afraid of any particular type of pet animal?

_____ 1. No, I like all animals.

_____ 2. Yes, I dislike/I am afraid of cats.

_____ 3. Yes, I dislike/I am afraid of dogs.

_____ 4. I dislike the following animals: _____

What problems, if any, do you think might arise if selected animals were allowed to visit on a regular basis? _____

_____

Where should animals not be allowed in your facility? (Animals are automatically excluded from any area where food is being served.) _____

_____

What benefits, if any, do you think there might be if selected animals were allowed to visit on a regular basis? _____

_____

Would you be willing to participate in a visiting animal program on a regular basis? Your participation might include showing animal handlers who to visit, determining which clients want an animal visit, helping a handler interact with a client, etc.

_____ Yes, I would be willing to participate.   _____ No, I am not willing to participate.

Please return this survey to: _____

This questionnaire can be used to screen staff & clients prior to initiation of an AAA/AAT program. Updated 1995.

Client Population Assessment

AAA/AAT

Section 1:   **Population Description**

Population: _____ Age Range: _____

Is the population a specific group within a group? Describe: _____

_____

Describe the general physical functioning level: _____

_____

Section 2:   **Population Needs**

What are the most important or unique concerns of this population? _____

_____

What do they have in common? _____

_____

What type of follow-up is needed with this population? _____

_____

Special considerations or precautions: _____

_____

What particular forms (consent, etc.) are required to work with this population? _____

_____

Section 3:   **Population Supports**

What are the unique advantages of this population? _____

_____

What problem areas are currently addressed: _____

_____

Can family support be provided? _____

Which allied fields might provide support? _____

Does the facility determine pet history prior to admission? (circle one) Yes / No

Will volunteers be a part of the program? (circle one) Yes / No

Section 4:   **Expectations**

Do the clients have time to participate? (circle one) Yes / No

Describe anticipated program outcomes: _____

_____

DELTA SOCIETY. Updated 1995.

Psychosocial Client Referral
AAT

Client's Name: _____

Therapist: _____ Psychiatrist: _____

Diagnosis: _____

Precautions: _____

Pertinent History:

(Please check all that apply)

_____ Physically abused   _____ Traumatic history

_____ Suicide Attempt(s)   _____ Poor impulse control

_____ Animal abuse   _____ Has had pets

_____ Other _____

Symptoms:

(Please check all that apply)

_____ Depression   _____ Withdrawn

_____ Anxiety   _____ Poor play skills

_____ High blood pressure   _____ Bland affect

_____ Poor short-term memory   _____ Uncommunicative

_____ Inappropriate touching   _____ Poor concentration

_____ Sexually preoccupied   _____ Religiously preoccupied

_____ Poor socialization skills   _____ Physically inactive/sedentary

_____ Lack of engagement in unit activities _____ Hyperactive

_____ Difficulty adjusting to hospital environment

_____ Delusions (briefly specify): _____

_____ Hallucinations (briefly specify): _____

_____ Other: _____

Adapted from Providence St. Peter Hospital, Olympia, WA, Jan. 1992.

Rehabilitation Treatment Plan
Animal-Assisted Therapy

Patient Name: _____ Age: _____ Room: _____

Diagnosis: _____

Therapist(s): _____ Physician: _____

Patient's present level of functioning (physical & cognitive): _____

_____

Work On: (Circle items)	R Upper Ext	L Upper Ext	R Lower Ext	L Lower Ext
Positioning: (Circle items)	Wheelchair	Mat	Bed	Other
Transfers Require:	Max Assist	Mod Assist	Min Assist	Stand-by Asst
	Contact Guard	Assist		

Therapeutic Activity Goals:

_____ Gross Motor Skills

_____ Fine Motor Skills

_____ Hand Strength and Coordination

_____ Cross Midline

_____ Sitting Balance

_____ Standing Balance

_____ Ambulation for feet

_____ Left Neglect Compensation

_____ Right Visual Field Cut Compensation

_____ Conversation/Verbal Communication

_____ Weight Shifting and Reaching:

    _____ Forwards/Backwards

    _____ Side to Side

    _____ Right Side

    _____ Left Side

_____ Requires Verbal Cues

_____ Requires Manual Assist

_____ Memory Retention

_____ Yes/No Verbal Response

_____ Verbal Repetition

_____ Communication Device

_____ Facial and Breathing Exercises

_____ Visual Tracking

_____ Other: _____

_____

_____

Comments: _____

_____

_____

Date: _____ Therapist's Initials: _____

Adapted from Providence St. Peter Hospital, Olympia, WA, 1995.

Appendix C: ANNOTATED BIBLIOGRAPHY

Proceedings

Burger, I., ed. <u>Pets, Benefits and Practice</u>. Waltham Symposium 20, April 1990. BVA Publications, December 1990.

Proceedings of a symposium held in Harrogate, United Kingdom, April 19, 1990 that examined issues surrounding the need for keeping companion animals and the positive health benefits derived from contact with animals.

Katcher, Aaron H. and Alan M. Beck, eds. <u>New Perspectives on Our Lives with Companion Animals</u>. Philadelphia: University of Pennsylvania Press, 1983.

Proceedings of the International Conference on the Human-Companion bond that took place at the University of Pennsylvania, October 5-7, 1981. Contains sections on the following: 1) Animals and People: The Tie Between; 2) A Social Predator for a Companion; 3) Society with Animals; 4) Companion Animals and Human Health; 5) The Loss of a Companion Animal; 6) Therapeutic Uses of Companion Animals; and 7) Context for Companion Animal Studies.

Rowan, Andrew N., ed. <u>Animals and People Sharing the World</u>. Hanover, New Hampshire. University Press of New England, 1988.

Selected contributions from speakers at the 1986 DELTA SOCIETY International Conference in Boston, Massachusetts.

Books

Arkow, P., ed. *The Loving Bond. Companion Animals In the Helping Professions.* Saratoga, CA. R and E Publishers. 1987.

A compilation of articles written by a wide variety of practitioners in AAA and AAT. A guidebook of useful, practical information for student and practitioner in any facility.

Arkow, P. *Pet Therapy: A Study and Resource Guide for the Use of Companion Animals in Selected Therapies.* Colorado Springs, CO: The Humane Society of Pikes Peak Region. Sixth Edition, 1990.

Excellent resource manual covering history, environments, applications, policies, implementation, evaluation, and legislation. Includes thorough resource guide.

Bernard, Shari. *Animal Assisted Therapy: A Guide for Health Care IT Professionals and Volunteers.* Whitehouse, TX: Therapet L.L.C, 1995.

A practical guidebook leading the reader through initiation of a program, selecting and testing animals, legal issues, documentation, volunteer recruitment and retention, volunteer and animal training, and safety.

Burch, Mary, Ph.D. *Volunteering with Your Pet.* New York, NY: Howell Book House/Macmillan USA, 1996.

Mary Burch discusses the elements of AAT, to help make the experience wonderful for all involved. The book gives in-depth information on getting started, including how to evaluate your pet and yourself to determine to what environment you are best suited. The book will inspire pet owners with creative ways to contribute to the lives of others.

Nebbe, Linda Lloyd. *Nature as a Guide: Using Nature in Counseling, Therapy, and Education.* Minneapolis: Educational Media Corporation, Second Edition, 1995.

This book contains an overview of animal-assisted activities and therapy as well as many practical applications that can be used with various populations.

Pet Partners Introductory Animal Handler Skills Course. Renton, WA: DELTA SOCIETY, 1995.

This course is a manual of general concerns and procedures for volunteers in animal-assisted activities and therapy programs. Chapters include: 1) Volunteers, 2) Animals, 3) Clients, 4) Visiting, and 5) Facilities. It includes an extensive glossary, articles, and resources, plus information on how to register with the Pet Partners Program.

Pet Partners Animal Evaluator Course. Renton, WA: DELTA SOCIETY, 1994.

This course is designed for people who have experience with a variety of different animal species and experience in Animal-Assisted Activities or Therapy (AAA/T) work. It teaches how animal behavior relates to AAA/T situations. This is only available as classroom instruction, not as a correspondence course.

Ruckert, Janet. *The Four-Footed Therapist. How your pet can help you solve your problems.* Berkeley, CA: Ten Speed Press, 1987.

A book of practical suggestions recognizing the healing power of animal companionship to assist with many every-day problems.

Periodicals

The Human-Animal Bond- Implications for Professional Nursing. *Holistic Nursing Practice*, January 1991. Volume 5, Number 2.

This issue is about the healing potential in the human-animal bond. It is about the positive health effects brought about by the opportunity to relate to and nurture an animal. The authors of this issue stress the relationship of the human-animal bond to the processes of coping, social support, family interaction, and health promotion.

Anthrozoos., A Multidisciplinary Journal on the Interactions of People, Animals, and Nature. 1987 - Present.

This is a quarterly publication whose focus is to report the results of studies from a wide array of disciplines on the interactions among people, animals, and nature. The fourth issue of each year includes a subject and author index.

Interactions

A publication of the DELTA SOCIETY. Each issue focuses on a human-animal bond topic and gives both research results and anecdotal information. Written for the general public as well as AAA/T Specialists.

Pet Partners Newsletter.
1991 – 1999 (Archived at www.deltasociety.org)

A publication of the DELTA SOCIETY. Written specifically to provide practical information for people volunteering or working in the field of AAA/T.

Other Resources

National Charities Information Bureau (From Standard 7.4)

Animal Welfare Act (From Standard 7.12)

Title 9, CFR (From Standard 8.1)

Information about the availability of the noted materials can be obtained by contacting DELTA SOCIETY, 875 124th Avenue NE, Suite 101, Bellevue, WA 98005-2531, phone 425-226-7357, email info@deltasociety.org or www.deltasociety.org.

Appendix D: GLOSSARY OF TERMS

Activity Director   The person responsible for planning recreational activities for people living in or attending programs at a facility.

Animal-Assisted Activities (AAA)

Activities that involve animals visiting people. The same activity can be repeated with different people, unlike a therapy program that is tailored to a particular person or medical condition.

AAA provide opportunities for motivational, educational, and/or recreational benefits to enhance quality of life. AAA are delivered in a variety of environments by a specially trained professional, paraprofessional, and/or volunteer in association with animals that meet specific criteria.

Animal-Assisted Therapy (AAT)

AAT involves a health or human service professional who uses an animal as part of his/her job. Specific goals for each client have been identified by the professional, and progress is measured and recorded.

AAT is a goal-directed intervention in which an animal meeting specific criteria is an integral part of the treatment process. AAT is delivered and/or directed by a health or human service provider working within the scope of his/her profession. AAT is designed to promote improvement in human physical, social, emotional, and/or cognitive functioning. AAT is provided in a variety of settings and may be group or individual in nature. The process is documented and evaluated.

Animal-Assisted Activity Specialist

A person who provides AAA and possesses specialized knowledge of animals and the populations with which they interact. The activities include animals and are motivationally, educationally and/or recreationally oriented.

Animal-Assisted Therapy Specialist

A health-care provider who delivers and/or directs Animal-Assisted Therapy (AAT). This person possesses expertise in incorporating animals as a treatment modality and is knowledgeable about animals. The AAT Specialist is credentialed and/or recognized by a separate human service professional discipline. This individual complies with the legal and ethical requirements of his/her profession as well as local, state, and federal laws relating to this work.

Animal Handler	A specially trained person, either paid or volunteer, who accompanies an animal during the course of AAA/AAT sessions. The animal handler's primary responsibility is to monitor and control the interaction between the client and animal.
Assessment	A process to determine the needs of the facility, client, or population receiving services. An evaluation prior to services being provided.
By-Laws	The rules or laws by which an organization operates.
Care Plan	The written plan of treatment for an individual client, including objectives and goals. Different health or human service professions have different names, including Individualized Education Plans (IEPS) in education, nursing care plans, habitation plans (for people with developmental disabilities), and others.
Caregiver	Someone, such as a physician, nurse, or social worker, who helps identify, prevent, or treat an illness or disability. A caregiver may also be a family member or friend providing care to a person at home or assisting in care at a facility.
Certification	An official confirmation that a person or animal has the minimum knowledge and/ or skills required to perform a certain task or work in a particular job. Certification is usually granted after passing a test. Sometimes proof of experience is also required. Certification is usually provided by an independent group or agency who is familiar with the requirements of the job. (See credentials, below.)

Certified Animal Evaluator

People who have been specially trained and certified by DELTA SOCIETY to perform the animal skills (PPST) and aptitude (PPAT) screenings required to register as a Pet Partners team.

Certified Therapeutic Recreation Specialist (CTRS)

A person with specialized training and national certification in therapeutic recreation. A CTRS provides therapeutic recreation training for clients. S/he sets specific goals for clients and measures their progress.

Client	A person who is receiving services from a health care or human service facility. The term "client" includes patients and residents of such facilities.

Credentials/Credentialled

> A testimonial that a person is entitled to act in an official capacity. (For example, a lawyer cannot practice law until after s/he has passed the bar exam.) A credential is usually not granted until a person has passed a test, and sometimes proved experience. (See certification, above.)

DELTA SOCIETY An international, not-for-profit organization of pet owners and health or human service professionals. Its mission is to promote *animals helping people* improve their health, independence, and quality of life.

Documentation A process for recording interactions and significant events, including date, participants, what took place, and recommendations for the future.

Evaluation A method to determine whether progress has been made toward previously stated goals.

Facility A health care or human service institution such as a hospital, nursing home (skilled nursing facility), school, correctional facility, residential care housing, counseling center, etc.

Fiduciary Responsibility

> The legal responsibility of a person or group who holds trust or is the trustee (board member) of an organization.

Goals As related to treatment or activity goals, a skill or accomplishment for the client to work toward.

Habilitation Plans Documents used in facilities for people with developmental disabilities to record a client's goals.

Health or Human Service Providers

> That group of people providing health care, or psychosocial, educational, motivational, recreational, and/or therapeutic services to people. These include, but are not limited to physicians, occupational therapists, physical therapists, recreational therapists, social workers, psychologists, counselors, and special educators.

Hospice	Health care for people with a life expectancy of six months or less. The focus is on relief of symptoms rather than cure. Physical, emotional, and spiritual support is provided to people who are terminally ill and their loved ones.

Immune Compromised

The inability of the body's natural defense system to fully fight off disease, making a person or animal extremely susceptible to infections. Unlike those same infections in healthy individuals, they are life threatening to people and animals who are immune compromised. Examples are patients receiving chemotherapy, patients with organ transplants, and patients with the AIDS virus.

Immunologist	A specially trained person who deals with people's ability to resist infection. A facility's immunologist provides in-service training and works with the facility regarding zoonoses and infection control.

Individualized Education Plans (IEPS)

Documents used in educational settings to record the goals and progress of school-aged children.

Infection Control	Policies and procedures that identify and address those situations that have the potential to spread disease. For example, hand washing is an infection control policy.
In-Service Training	Continuing education provided to people involved in providing services to a client population group.
Nursing Care Plans	Documents used in nursing homes to record the goals of clients.
Objective	The aim or end of an action; the method used to reach therapeutic goals. An example is, "The client will comb the dog, making three strokes with the left hand."

Occupational Therapist (OT)

A specially trained and credentialled person who works on physical, social, and cognitive (thinking) skills with clients. This may include daily living skills (e.g., eating, meal preparation, cleaning, etc.) and vocational skills. OTs also help people regain the use of their hands and upper body, and increase range of motion (how much someone can move a particular body part.)

Pathogen	Bacteria, fungus, or other microorganism that causes disease.
Pet Partners	A national and international program of the DELTA SOCIETY which trains people, and screens people-animal teams for suitability in AAA/AAT programs. Pet Partner teams receive a photo ID badge, pet tag, *Interactions* (a Delta Society publication), and liability insurance. Pet Partners must renew and be re-evaluated every two years.

Physical Therapist (PT)

A specially trained and credentialled person who works on improving movement that uses the larger muscle groups. S/he may help a client strengthen his/her legs and walk.

Policies and Procedures

Written wisdom guiding the management of affairs. A definite course of action to be taken.

Treatment Team	A variety of health-care providers who work with a client to provide complete treatment services. This team may include, among others, a physician, nurse, OT, and social worker.
Utilization Review	An accountability process to determine if the services offered to clients meet the needs of those clients.

Zoonotic Diseases (Zoonoses)

Illnesses that can be transmitted from animals to humans or humans to animals.

Standards of Practice for AAA/AAT

Appendix E: **TASK FORCE MEMBERS**

The following people are gratefully acknowledged for their participation in the initial task force to develop standards for Animal-Assisted Activities and Animal-Assisted Therapy from 1990 - 1992.

Robert J. Behling, Ph.D.
Joliet, IL

Guy Hancock, D.V.M.
Seminole, FL

Sherry Kirwin, M.S.
Galveston, TX

Judith Gammonley, RNC, Ed.D.
Palm Harbor, FL

Pearl Salotto-Lester
Henrietta, NY

Bonnie S. Mader, M.S.
Davis, CA

Ann R. Howie, ACSW
Tumwater, WA

Deborah Cobalis
Austin, TX

Linda Lloyd Nebbe, M.S.
Cedar Falls, IA

Final revisions and writing completed by:
Ann Howie, ACSW and Maureen Fredrickson, M.S.W.

Appendix F: SAMPLE GOALS AND METHODS

Sample Rehabilitation

Animal-Assisted Therapy Goals and Methods

TREATMENT GOALS	METHODS
Improve shoulder flexion	Patient sits in chair and grooms animal, which is placed on table. Child sits on floor and grooms large dog (e.g., Great Dane) while it is standing.
Improve upper extremity abduction	Animal is placed on the patient's affected side. Patient pets and grooms animal.
Improve supination	Patient throws ball underhanded to dog. Position animal on patient's affected side. Patient strokes animal's underbelly with the palm of his hand.
Improve fine motor skills	Patient feeds small pieces of food to bird. Patient manipulates buckles, clasps on leashes, collars, and animal carriers. Patient opens containers with treats for the animals.
Improve crawling/perambulation	Child crawls to animal that is placed in his visual field.
Begin ambulation skills	Patient ambulates to animal placed at a designated station or at the end of parallel bars.
Improve wheelchair skills	Patient places animal on lap and wheels to designated station or through an obstacle course.
Improve quality of gait	Patient functions as animal handler and does basic obedience skills with dog under handler supervision. Animal is placed at a station and patient ambulates to the animal.

Improve standing balance	Patient grooms or pets animal while patient is standing independently or in standing frame.
Improve trunk control	Patient reaches to get grooming equipment and bring self to sitting position. Patient reaches to pet or groom animal positioned away from patient. When finished with activity, patient hands the animal to someone else.
Improve safe use of walker	Patient puts brush, treats, leash, and collar in walker basket and ambulates to animal.

Sample Rehabilitation Treatment Plan Including AAT

PROBLEM 1	Limited standing and walking tolerance
Objective:	With a quadruped cane for support, the client's balance to improve and standing tolerance to increase to 30 minutes.
Method:	Walk a large dog for short distances around facility grounds and/or through halls using a Velcro mitt on affected hand for holding the leash with facilitative assistance.
PROBLEM 2	Limited scapula mobility and shoulder ROM
Objective:	Decrease spasticity and increase scapula mobility so that 120 degree shoulder flexion and abduction is possible.
Method:	Using a Velcro mitt on affected side, assist client in bilateral grasp of a large animal brush, achieving elbow extension with shoulder flexion and scapula protraction. Position dog in front of client. Direct client to bring the brush from the dog's head to his tail repeatedly.
PROBLEM 3	Right visual field deficit
Objective:	Client to spontaneously compensate for visual field deficit 80 percent of the treatment time.
Method:	Position client at a narrow table with another table of various sized collars and leashes immediately on his right side; affected arm positioned forward, used for weight bearing. Direct the client to reach across his body and select the appropriate collar, leash, etc. for the dog; also facilitates trunk rotation and visual attention to affected side. Therapist should stand on affected side when talking with the client or giving instructions.

PROBLEM 4	Lack of coordination in non-dominant upper extremity
Objective:	Improve left hand coordination so that client can legibly and with ease write his name and address.
Method:	Manipulating snaps on leashes and buckles on collars. Also grasping small comb to comb long-haired animal.

PROBLEM 5	Mild expressive aphasia
Objective 1:	Name common household objects within realm of everyday activities with 90 percent accuracy.
Method:	Name objects used for grooming tasks, name objects used for preparation of animal's meal.
Objective 2:	Verbalize function and uses of objects targeted in Objective 1 with 90 percent accuracy.
Method:	Verbalize function and use of specific grooming tools and meal-preparation utensils.

PROBLEM 6	Inability to plan leisure activities
Objective:	At discharge, client will contact three identified leisure resources within his community.
Method:	Explore leisure opportunities with therapists familiar with volunteer opportunities related to animals (i.e., humane societies, animal shelters, and Pet Partners programs).

Prepared by Sherry Kirwin, Moody Gardens, Galveston, TX, 1995.

Sample Psychotherapy

Animal-Assisted Therapy Goals and Techniques

TREATMENT GOALS	AAT TECHNIQUES
Improve Socialization, Communication	• Practice teaching an animal something new
Reduce Isolation, Boredom, Loneliness	• Engage in play with an animal
	• Learn about and then assist in the care/grooming/ feeding of an animal. Reminisce about the past
	• Remember and repeat information about the animal

- Learn about animal, then take animal around and
- Verbally introduce animal to others
- Take animal for a walk (outside, around unit, around room, etc.)
- Receive apparent acceptance from an animal
- Give appropriate affection to an animal

Brighten Affect and Mood	• Receive apparent acceptance from an animal
Lessen Depression	• Engage in play with an animal
Provide Pleasure, Affection	• Spend time caring for/ grooming an animal
	• Take animal for a walk
Improve Reality Orientation	• Take animal around and introduce animal to others
	• Give affection to an animal
	• Interact with (pet, talk to, groom, etc.) an animal
	• Play with an animal
	• Give and receive affection from an animal
	• Reminisce about the past
	• Verbally introduce animal to others
	• Take animal for a (supervised) walk (outside, around unit, around room, etc.)
	• Remember and repeat information about the animal
	• Talk about animals person has known
	• Describe animal
	• Follow sequence of instructions with animal
	• Give animal verbal commands or hand signals
	• Ask questions about animal, animal's care
Decrease Manipulative Behaviors	• Observe animal behaviors
	• Education about the meaning of animal behavior(s)
	• Observe and discuss animals' response to human behavior (immediate consequences)

- Practice teaching an animal something new

- Develop a cooperative plan to accomplish something with an animal

- Organize equipment needed to accomplish a task (grooming, go around obstacles, etc.)

- Generalize animal behavior to human circumstances

- Forecast "what would happen if...?"

- Engage in play with an animal

Address Grieving/Loss Issues

- Talk about animals the person has known

- Reminisce about past animal loss(es)

- Discuss how animals might feel when their animal companion dies/when baby animals leave their mother's etc.

Improve Ability to Express Feelings

- Observe animal behavior(s)

- Education about the meaning of animal behavior(s)

- Give appropriate affection to an animal

- Receive affection from an animal

- Observe and discuss animal's response to human behavior

- Discuss how animals might feel if their mother left them/if the other animals don't like them etc. (relate to client's circumstances)

- Talk about animals the person has known

- Generalize animal behavior to human circumstances

- Forecast "how do you think the animal is feeling?"

Reduce Abusive Behavior

- Learn about and then assist in the care/grooming/feeding of an animal

Improve Ability to Trust

- Education about the meaning of animal behavior(s), Interpret animal behavior as it happens

Learn About Appropriate Touch

- Practice teaching an animal something new

- Observe and discuss animal's response to human behavior

- Learn gentle ways to handle animals

- Receive apparent acceptance from an animal

- Give affection to an animal

- Develop a cooperative plan to accomplish something with an animal

- Follow sequence of instructions with an animal

- Generalize animal behavior to human circumstances

- Forecast "what would happen if...?"

Improve Memory, Recall

- Reminisce about animals person has known

- Ask questions about animal, animal's care

- Remember and repeat information about the animal

- Describe an animal

- Follow a sequence of instructions with animal

Improve Cooperation

- Learn about and then assist in the care/grooming/feeding of an animal

Improve Problem-Solving Ability

- Practice teaching an animal something new

- Observe and discuss animal's response to human behavior

- Develop a cooperative plan to accomplish something with an animal

- Follow a sequence of instructions with an animal

- Organize equipment needed to accomplish a task

- Forecast "what would happen if ...?"

Prepared by Ann Howie, Providence St. Peter Hospital, Olympia, WA, 1995.